COURAGE TO BE FIRST

The Journey of Mid-Columbia Medical Center
in The Dalles, Oregon
Becoming the First Planetree Hospital
in America

Mark Scott

Leland Kaiser, Ph.D.

with **Richard Baltus**

SECOND RIVER
HEALTHCARE PRESS

Courage to Be First
The Journey of Mid-Columbia Medical Center in The Dalles, Oregon
Becoming the First Planetree Hospital in America

Second River Healthcare Press
26 Shawnee Way, Suite C
Bozeman, MT 59715

Phone (406) 586-8775
FAX   (406) 586-5672

Editor: Diane Dannenfeldt
Cover Design: Christopher R. Jackson
Cover Art: Lan Weisberger
Typesetting/Composition: Neuhaus/Tyrrell Graphic Design

Scott, Mark & Kaiser, Leland R., Ph.D., with Baltus, Richard
Courage to Be First: The Journey of Mid-Columbia Medical Center in The Dalles, Oregon Becoming the First Planetree Hospital in America / Mark Scott, Leland R. Kaiser, Ph.D., Richard Baltus

ISBN-10: 0-9814605-4-2 (hard cover)   ISBN-10: 0-9814605-5-0 (soft cover)
ISBN-13: 978-0-9814605-4-3 (hard cover)   ISBN-13: 978-0-9814605-5-0 (soft cover)

1. Planetree   2. Leadership   3. Health Services Administration

Library of Congress Control Number: 2008943705

First Printing: March 2009

Second River Healthcare Press books are available at special quantity discounts. Please call for information at: (406) 586-8775 or order from the websites:

www.SecondRiverHealthcare.com
www.CourageToBeFirst.com

TABLE OF CONTENTS

INTRODUCTIONS:

COURAGE TO BE FIRST:

A Moving "Forward"

Gary Adamson

What is possible here? That question has been with humankind since the beginning. And whether the subject is new methods of hunting and gathering or new ways of connecting the six billion people that inhabit the planet, all progress starts with that single question: What is possible here?

Possibility is an exciting thing to ponder. But it is also fraught with many obstacles and doubts: "We couldn't possibly *do* that," or worse, "We couldn't possibly *be* that." Most often, the practitioners of the currently esteemed "best practice" in any field are the ones who stand most firmly against "radical" change. That is a fact filled with irony, since all best practices of today were radical approaches just yesterday.

In the 1900s, conventional wisdom held that man couldn't fly. In the 1910s, conventional wisdom thought that mass-producing reliable, non-horse-drawn transportation was impossible. In the '50s, it was believed that man could not climb Mount Everest or run a mile in under four minutes. (Sir Edmund Hillary and Roger Bannister proved conventional wisdom wrong on both counts within six months of each other.) In the '60s, it was widely held that America was hopelessly behind the Russians in the space race. Looking back, much of what passed for irrefutable conventional wisdom seems silly today. And yet, we are just as limited by our own conventional wisdom as the leaders in the technology field during the '70s, who boldly predicted the need for as many as six computers in the world.

If you doubt this is so, let's engage in a simple thought experiment. I want you to think about a typical 50-bed hospital. That shouldn't be too hard to do since there are many of them in this country. Now that you have that image in your mind, let me ask you some questions about it. What does it look like? What kind of technology does it have? From how far away do patients come? How successful is it in recruiting highly respected physicians from throughout the country? And most importantly, has it made many nationally recognized innovations in healthcare?

Conventional wisdom holds that a 50-bed hospital can't do most of these things at all, much less do them exceptionally. And yet, you are holding in your hands the story of a 49-bed hospital that was the second place in the United States, after Memorial Sloan-Kettering Cancer Center, to implement intensity-modulated radiation therapy (IMRT) technology; has drawn patients from 28 states; has recruited heads of departments from leading academic medical centers to practice there; and has hosted more than 2,000 site visits for people coming from all over the world to study its innovations. This is the impossible story of Mid-Columbia Medical Center (MCMC), a 49-bed hospital located in The Dalles, Oregon. Impossible except for one thing: The people at MCMC didn't think it was impossible, and they were right.

Jim Goodwin put it this way: "The impossible is often just the untried." The Chinese have a saying that goes: "Those who are busy talking about how something is impossible should not interrupt those who are busy doing it." In both cases, confident, persistent action, based on passionately held beliefs, is what separates people who make discoveries from those who get news about them. In the case of MCMC, it started with the co-author of this book, Leland Kaiser, Ph.D., and the architect of MCMC's transformation, Mark Scott. Both of them have had a great affect on me — Lee, as the head of my graduate school program in health administration and Mark as my business partner in Starizon.

One of the great privileges of my life is having each of them as a colleague, a mentor and a friend. Knowing them the way I do, I am certain that this book was not written to brag and boast about the exploits of MCMC, although I am sure they are both proud of what is happening there. No, they wrote this book as a personal challenge to you — a challenge to defy the gravitational pull of conventional wisdom that keeps you stuck in doing the old way harder; a challenge to believe in your thoughts and your ideals; and a challenge to act now, and act forcefully, because the future of your company and your industry depends on it.

MCMC's story is not a fairy tale that happened in a far-off land that you cannot visit. Instead, it is meant as an inspiring story of possibility that concludes with this thought, "If they can do it, why can't we?"

THE IMPORTANCE OF MARK SCOTT, MID-COLUMBIA MEDICAL CENTER, THIS BOOK AND WHAT MIGHT FOLLOW FROM IT

LELAND R. KAISER, PH.D.

This seems like a long title, but then again a lot is going on between the covers of this book. It is a book that will change your life — if you permit it to do so. It is a saga of the past. More importantly, it is a road map for the future.

The book had a beginning. It has no foreseeable end. What do I mean by this? It's simple. By reading the book, you become part of our story. What you do then, as a result of reading this book, is up to you, but in any case, it is part of our continuing story. Your future contribution to our book is unforeseeable to me. This part of our story, you must decide.

Mark Scott

I have known Mark Scott in many capacities over many years — as a friend, colleague, client, mentee, supporter of Estes Park Institute and as a Knight of the Healthcare Roundtable. Mark is the central character of this book. However, my treatment of Mark is not biographical. Mark is a human being just like you and me. He has strengths and weaknesses, as we all do. What I will describe is Mark's key role at Mid-Columbia Medical Center (MCMC). I will also use Mark as an example of many of the key qualities of a visionary, transformational leader. This treatment will make Mark appear a little larger than life. Please forgive me for that. I am not his biographer — simply an admirer, observer and friend.

Although Mark is no longer the CEO of MCMC, he continues to be very active in the field of environmental design. He left a legacy that the current managers of MCMC are carrying on. In addition, Mark is doing pioneering work at Starizon. I asked Mark to include a chapter in this book on the incredibly important work of Starizon. It is indeed a bright star on the horizon of designed experience in healthcare facilities, corporations and human groups.

MCMC

As a result of the work of Mark Scott and his management team, MCMC evolved into a destination hospital. That a small, rural Oregon hospital could do such a thing is a wonder in itself. It is a living testimony to the fact that radical innovations in healthcare do not depend upon a hospital's size, location or wealth. They depend upon the expanding consciousness of the CEO and his or her team.

By a destination hospital, I mean a place that pioneers an approach to patient care, generates nationwide interest and becomes a visitation site for hundreds of visitors who come to study and emulate its operation.

This Book

This book may be variously viewed as a historical saga, a philosophic treatise, a plunge into the metaphysics of management, an operations manual for designed environments or a road map to the future of community hospitals in America. In a sense, it is all of these and yet none of them, really. It is simply a story that wanted to be told. I have the great privilege of telling this story with my friends and co-authors, Mark Scott and Dick Baltus. We have started and stopped this joint storytelling effort many times. For many months, our joint effort seemed to have died — and then like the phoenix, it arose from the ashes. I am not really sure why we could not give up trying to tell this story. We are both waiting to find out what will come from our efforts.

What Might Follow

Mark Scott, Gary Adamson, Dick Baltus and I have ideas about continuing this book through periodic updates. We will have to wait and see. I don't know for sure why the book is here. I am even less certain about where it will take us. As our reader, do you have any ideas? If so, please drop us a line at CourageToBeFirst.com.

STAGING THE HEALTHCARE EXPERIENCE

B. JOSEPH PINE II

Today, goods and services are being commoditized everywhere. Therefore, it's time to move beyond goods and services to a new level of economic value — and that means staging experiences for individual customers. Experiences are a distinct economic offering, as distinct from services as services are from goods. Experiences occur when goods and services are used as props, as the stage to engage each individual in an inherently personal way and thereby create a memory, the hallmark of the experience. We are moving into an experience economy, where experiences are becoming the predominant economic offering.

As I travel the globe explaining this fundamental shift in the very fabric of the economy — and researching all sorts of new and wondrous experiences around the world, I often have to point out that I didn't *invent* the experience economy; rather, I *discovered* it. I discovered what executives and managers were doing to respond to the commoditization of their goods and services and to create economic value, and then I built frameworks to show everyone else what was going on and to figure out what they should do about it.

One such executive who was way ahead of the game was Mark Scott. As CEO of Mid-Columbia Medical Center in The Dalles, Oregon, he was one of the first — if not the first — in the healthcare industry to foresee that staging a more engaging, less stressful and highly valued hospital experience was the way out of the morass in which the industry found itself after the rise of managed care. Research has shown that better experiences lead to better outcomes, and that is the bottom line for this industry where what patients and their family members want most is to be transformed.

What is also clear is that the MCMC experience is one that its patients perceive as authentic. And that's the key thing that I, and my co-author Jim Gilmore, have discovered since the publication of *The Experience Economy* in 1999. In a world of paid-for experiences, people increasingly question what is real and what is not. They no longer accept the fake from the phony; they want the real from the genuine. In today's experience economy, managing the perception of authenticity has become the number-one business imperative.

B. Joseph Pine II is principal innovator for Starizon and co-author of *The Experience Economy* and *Authenticity: What Consumers Really Want.*

PREFACE

MARK SCOTT

During my tenure as president and CEO of Mid-Columbia Medical Center, I would often leave my office at the end of a long day and jump on my bike for a ride along the back roads of The Dalles.

Just a few blocks away from MCMC, you can turn onto Scenic Drive and head up the hill toward Sorosis Park. I would stop there often to take in the spectacular panoramic view of The Dalles — the tree-lined neighborhoods below, then the historic downtown and, just beyond that, the beautiful, but imposing, Columbia River.

On most of these early evenings, the Columbia River Gorge's famous east wind would be blowing; it's a rare day in The Dalles when there's not at least a breeze.

I remember one day in particular, stopping at the top of the hill in front of the park and straddling my bike, just to unwind a little while taking in the scenery. The waters of the Columbia were especially choppy on this day; the river was really churning. As I watched the wind kicking up the whitecaps, suddenly my thoughts turned to Lewis and Clark, the explorers who nearly 200 years earlier had passed through The Dalles toward the end of the greatest expedition in the history of this country.

I found myself wondering what it must have been like for the brave members of the Corps of Discovery negotiating the infamous Long and Short Narrows (Grandes Dalles de la Columbia) for which The Dalles was named.

In his journal, Clark wrote apprehensively about the prospect of guiding canoes through what would be the most dangerous stretch of the Columbia River the Corps would encounter:

"The whole of the Current of this great river must at all Stages pass thro' this narrow chanel of 45 yards wide. As the portage of our canoes over this high rock would be impossible... accordingly I deturmined to pass through this place notwithstanding the horrid appearance of this agitated gut Swelling, boiling and whorling in every direction (which from the top of the rock did not appear as bad as when I was in it)."

As I stood there within eyeshot of where these explorers successfully came ashore in one piece, I was awestruck by the courage it took to be one of those explorers — to be part of a team setting out on a journey with virtually no idea what they would encounter. To be a Lewis or Clark cutting a path across a continent or a Magellan setting out around the world, guided only by primitive maps with foreboding drawings of dragons indicating the end of man's exploration to that point. Or, to be any of the scores of other explorers possessed of the courage to be first to venture into the unknown.

And now it occurred to me that exploration was the perfect metaphor for the transformation then underway at Mid-Columbia Medical Center. At this moment in time, we were a few years into our efforts to dramatically improve the hospital experience for our patients.

Though we faced no danger other than failure, the journey our organization set out on in the late 1980s certainly required a leap of faith by our own corps of intrepid explorers.

When we took up the challenge of becoming the first hospital to implement the Planetree concept of care organization-wide, none of us completely understood what lay ahead. But we knew that the journey had the potential to change us all dramatically and, in the process, help us discover a new and, we felt, better model of care for our community.

It took the courage of an entire organization, and many others from outside of it, to accomplish what we had up to the point of that bike ride to Sorosis Park. And on that windy day on the hill it occurred to me that perhaps Lewis and Clark had left something behind when they passed through The Dalles on their way to the Pacific Ocean. Whether it was some of their DNA or just the spirit of being the first to try something, without any promise of success, I knew their same spirit of exploration was alive and well at MCMC.

In the years since, the organization has continued to venture where other hospitals have not, continually pushed forward by people with the courage to enter uncharted waters.

CHAPTER 1

AN UNLIKELY SETTING

"Before the narrows, where the river widened, the party made camp on a high point of rocks. The captains chose the site because it formed a kind of fortification. Clark explained, 'this Situation we Concieve well Calculated for defence.' They called it 'Fort Rock Camp' (located on the site of today's city named The Dalles, Oregon). There they stayed for three days to make repairs."

– Stephen E. Ambrose
Undaunted Courage: Meriwether Lewis, Thomas Jefferson
and the Opening of the American West

To reach the small, rural Oregon community of The Dalles from the state's largest city, Portland, the traveler follows Interstate 84 east for 80 miles, passing through some of the most breathtaking scenery on the continent.

Interstate 84 stretches across the top of the state, flanked to the south by towering cliffs covered in evergreens and accented with several waterfalls, and to the north by the Columbia River and, on its far side, the state of Washington.

Thirty minutes outside Portland, at the western entrance to the Columbia River Gorge National Scenic Area, the water of the magnificent Multnomah Falls spills over the top of Larch Mountain and plummets 620 feet to earth, creating the second-tallest, year-round waterfall in the United States.

Another 30 minutes brings the visitor to Hood River, which, until the mid-1980s, was a sleepy town in the shadow of Mount Hood known primarily for its bountiful orchards and nearly incessant wind. But not long after someone affixed a sail to a surfboard, Hood River, and its ideal combination of wind and water, was discovered by adventurous outsiders. In short order, it was transformed into the "windsurfing capital of the world," and in the years since, the community of approximately 6,000 has grown into a popular destination for tourists and seasonal residents.

Just five miles east of Hood River, the scenery of "The Gorge" changes suddenly and dramatically. The perpendicular, tree-covered cliffs quickly taper down to bare, rolling hills. While the landscape of the previous 60 miles resembles a continuous — and universally appealing — postcard, the view as you pass the Cascade Mountain Range and head into the drier climate of eastern Oregon is far less impressive.

Mark Scott, the chief executive officer of Mid-Columbia Medical Center in The Dalles, was well aware of the effect that this change in scenery could have on visitors to the region. So, in the late 1980s, Scott first charted what became known as the "Physician Recruit Scenic Tour." Scott's employee chauffeurs, who were sent to Portland to pick up physicians on recruiting visits, were instructed to leave I-84 at Mosier, just east of Hood River, and head back into the hills. It was a more circuitous route than following the freeway, to be sure, but it took the newcomers along the old scenic highway and delivered them through the lush fruit orchards that line the beautiful backdoor entrance to The Dalles.

By contrast, if you stay on I-84 for the full 20-minute trip from Hood River to The Dalles, the view from the freeway is of a town that could benefit from a good coat of paint. Locals and frequent visitors know there is more to The Dalles than first meets the eye, but Scott knew the value of the first impression. When he brought a physician to town, he went to great lengths to stage a memorable experience. Recruiting physicians to small communities was difficult in the best of circumstances, and Scott didn't want some minor detail out of his control — like the view of a trailer court from the freeway — to lessen the impact of the most effective recruiting tool he had: the remarkably innovative hospital he was running.

Until acclaimed journalist Bill Moyers brought his television crew to town in 1992 to film a segment of a PBS series that would introduce Mid-Columbia Medical Center to a worldwide audience, The Dalles was known — at least among history buffs — for one thing: Lewis and Clark slept here.

The pioneers who followed the famed explorers west during the early 1800s would establish The Dalles as the terminus of the Oregon Trail. This was the spot where the brave travelers would decide whether to proceed west by land or negotiate the sometimes treacherous Columbia River. The Dalles was a place where many passed through, but few stayed. Two hundred years later, that would still serve as an appropriate description for the town.

The population of The Dalles hovered around 12,000 for several decades of the 1900s. With wheat ranchers, farmers, orchardists and a hospital at the core of its local economy, the community has always persevered but has rarely thrived. In the late 1990s, an aluminum plant injected life into the local economy, but when the industry took a nose dive, it took the plant down with it.

Just 20 minutes down the freeway, Hood River has used its ever-present wind and water resources to power significant economic development. But The Dalles has resisted attempting the same, though the same gales and river pass through it.

This is not to say The Dalles is devoid of progress. In recent years, federal dollars have built a shiny new post office across from the stately old post office, helped replace downtown sidewalks and streetlights with decorative pavers and Victorian-style lamps, and funded a new gateway under the freeway linking downtown with the waterfront.

After standing abandoned for years, The Commodore, at four stories one of the tallest buildings in town, was given a handsome makeover at the start of the new millennium. With comfortable apartments above and contemporary commercial spaces below, The Commodore instantly became the architectural jewel of The Dalles' downtown. More recently, in 2006, Internet icon Google shocked the business world by choosing The Dalles as the site of a massive server farm. The decision sent national trade journalists scrambling for their atlases and left The Dalles' civic leaders optimistic that other new businesses would follow Google to town.

Despite recent signs that significant change may be in the offing for The Dalles, for most of its history, the community never would have been mistaken for progressive. Certainly no one ever would have predicted that it would be the home of a hospital that many consider among the most innovative in the world.

When Mark Scott arrived in The Dalles in 1978, he was, like most of the pioneers before him, just planning to pass through. It was to be a brief layover that could take him one step closer to a career as a healthcare consultant, advising hospitals on how to streamline their operating rooms.

Years earlier, Scott had stumbled into the healthcare industry for wont of any better option. After growing up in Salt Lake City, he studied at Utah State University. Scott majored in both political science and business, and at the end of four years, had his bachelor's degree. Still, he hadn't found a focus. He had been accepted into Utah State's master's in business administration program, but he wasn't convinced that this was the path he was meant to travel.

So, when out of the blue, the brother of one of Scott's childhood friends (and the chief operating officer of Salt Lake City's Latter Day Saints Hospital) called with a job offer, Scott thought, "Why not?"

With one phone call, he went from college grad without a plan to associate director of surgery, second in command of a large operating department.

"It was just a big place, with a huge budget and lots of employees, and we worked all hours of the day and night," Scott remembered.

He loved the fast-paced environment of the surgery department, managing people and finances, and learning the art of building relationships with physicians. It would prove to be invaluable training.

Scott had married right out of college, and he and his wife, Jacque, a registered nurse, were living in a housing complex the hospital provided for its resident physicians. Scott, a former high-school quarterback, was recruited to play on the residents' flag football team. During a contest against the residents from the University of Utah Medical School, Scott met a physician with ties to the University of Oregon School of Medicine (now Oregon Health & Science University, or OHSU) in Portland. He learned that Oregon's only medical school was looking for an experienced operating-room supervisor to direct the merger of the university's hospital with a former county hospital.

Scott landed the job, and he and Jacque moved to Portland in 1975. He had found his niche in surgical department management and was soon consulting with other hospitals. Scott was hired at OHSU by Gary Rood, the associate director of the medical school hospital. In 1976, Rood left the university to become CEO of The Dalles General Hospital. (Rood would soon change the name to Mid-Columbia Medical Center, or MCMC.) When it was time to reorganize the small hospital's operating room, Rood knew whom to call for consulting help.

Every other weekend for six months, Scott drove to The Dalles to help direct the project. Then Rood approached him with another job offer. Scott would be the hospital's new chief operating officer, Rood's second in command. Sensing a good resume-building opportunity, Scott accepted, and in 1976 he and Jacque both began new jobs at the small community hospital in The Dalles.

"I thought it would be a good chance to get more experience working with physicians and a board of directors, and managing departments other than the OR," Scott said. "I figured I'd do that for about three years, and then I'd leave and really crank up this surgery consulting business."

But three years turned to seven and then, in 1983, Rood announced he would be leaving MCMC to start his own long-term-care business. Rood told Scott he wanted to recommend to the MCMC board that Scott move up to the top spot. Scott figured his consulting business had already waited this long, so what difference would a few more years make? And, besides, "hospital CEO" would look even better on his resume.

Scott inherited from Rood a solid, if unremarkable, community hospital that since its opening in 1959 had been the primary source of medical care for the 35,000 residents of rural Wasco and Sherman counties.

Rood had been recruited to inject some life into the hospital, which had been treading water for several years before his arrival. By the time Rood left in 1985, MCMC was in much better shape, providing a higher quality of care and in possession of an expanded medical staff and healthier bottom line.

However, the healthcare industry, as a whole, was more unsettled. Hospitals across the nation were struggling to rapidly increase their efficiencies, an absolute requirement for success after the introduction in the early 1980s of Medicare's prospective payment system. The federal government was holding hospitals more accountable for their charges to the Medicare program, categorizing medical conditions into 500-plus "diagnosis-related groups" and putting a cap on how much hospitals would be reimbursed for providing care. Efficient hospitals that could keep their patient care costs below Medicare reimbursement levels would be rewarded in the new system, but getting there wouldn't be easy in an industry that wasn't accustomed to dealing with change.

Medicare's new rules would help usher in one of the most tumultuous eras in the hospital industry's history. Following Medicare's lead, private insurance companies also began tightening the screws during contract negotiations, seeking to cap their payments to hospitals as well. Physicians were beginning to band together to create more clout in their dealings with hospitals.

To improve their efficiencies and lower their costs, hospitals began shifting as much care as possible into the less expensive outpatient setting. Many hospital administrators, searching for new sources of revenue, began developing new, nontraditional "product lines." Suddenly, hospital food service departments were also dabbling in private catering; grounds-keepers were out in the neighborhoods selling landscaping services.

In communities and regions served by more than one hospital, the traditional, collegial atmosphere gave way to intense competition for patients. For the first time in their history, many hospitals began implementing aggressive marketing programs to woo patients. Hospitals determined to cling to the status quo, unable to improve their operational efficiencies or losing their battles for patients, were at significant risk. Many closed.

This was not an easy time to be a hospital CEO, especially a new one. Scott learned early on that the job of a hospital CEO was all consuming.

"I remember Gary telling me, 'When you slide into that No. 1 chair, you're really going to have to amp up your hours,'" Scott said. "And I thought I'd handle it just fine, but that was just arrogance talking. I learned that even if you're not at the office working 12 hours a day, you're thinking about your job. Because almost every decision you make is a big deal.

"I was in control of millions of dollars, and the decisions I was making were affecting more than 600 employees and thousands of patients. And as the largest employer in the area, we made a tremendous impact on our community's economic fortunes. So I learned really quickly that if you like your work as a hospital CEO and you're really dedicated to it, the job can just consume you."

This is not to say Scott wasn't having his share of fun. He had always been competitive, and if the hospital industry was going to become a battleground of sorts, Scott wasn't afraid of a little hand-to-hand combat.

There had always been a natural rivalry between The Dalles and its more urbane neighbor downstream, Hood River. Typically, the battles were friendly and waged over the likes of which high school fielded the better sports team or which orchard produced the better fruit or which community had the better winds for the sailboarders.

In eras past, the communities' respective hospitals had always peacefully coexisted. Because The Dalles was roughly twice the size of Hood River, it had the larger hospital, the more advanced technology and a greater array of specialists on its medical staff. As a result, MCMC had grabbed a significant share of the Hood River market. Still, there had always been enough patients to go around.

By the late 1980s, however, that was no more a reality in the Columbia River Gorge than it was in any other multiple-hospital community in the United States. Scott knew that the good old days — when a hospital could simply open its front door and wait for the patients to stream in — were gone and that the rules of the game had changed forever. By the time Scott had assembled, virtually overnight, a prefab urgent-care center on the vacant lot directly across the street from his competitor, Hood River Memorial Hospital officials also knew the rules had changed.

Around Mid-Columbia Medical Center, the construction of the "Care Corner" became known as the shot heard 'round The Gorge. The facility housed not only the urgent care center, but also offices for primary care and specialty physicians whose job was to direct their patients back to The Dalles for hospital tests, medical care and other services.

The strategy was old hat in larger cities across the country and a no-brainer for Scott, who knew what was happening elsewhere to other hospitals that had shown they weren't fit for battle. But from that moment forward, there would no longer be anything friendly about the rivalry between MCMC and Hood River Memorial Hospital.

"At the time, we had a kick-ass mission statement that said, in a nutshell, 'We compete; we win. We survive; you don't,'" Scott said. "There was a real concern about whether the Columbia Gorge region could support two hospitals. And if one community was going to be without a hospital, it damn well wasn't going to be my community. Competing successfully for insurance contracts was critical to our success, but to do that, we needed to have a clinical presence in Hood River."

If building Care Corner was a brazen strategy, it also was a sound one that helped position MCMC for long-term success.[1]

But healthcare in the Columbia Gorge would never be the same. "It created an incredible explosion of competition and nastiness," Scott said.

By the late 1980s, Mark Scott's serious playing days were far behind him, but he was not yet 40 and remained a fairly intense athlete. His golf handicap never strayed from the low single digits; he was an avid racquetball player; and he had climbed most of the mountains in the Pacific Northwest. Whenever possible, Scott rode his bicycle to work, often lugging his beloved black Labrador Bo in a trailer behind him.

It was no surprise, then, that when he donned the uniform of a hospital CEO, Scott had no trouble gearing up for competition. He took on all comers — from fellow hospital administrators to physicians and from insurers to politicians, to any other person in possession of such poor judgment that they would attempt to stand between Scott and the particular goal he was defending. Scott was that opponent you hated to play against but would have loved to have on your team.

For about four years, he was seriously into the game. Scott supported his Care Corner venture with an aggressive marketing campaign in Hood River that featured clever billboards targeting the young newcomers who came to ride the waves and sometimes injured themselves. Scott knew that, unlike some longtime Hood River residents, the newcomers weren't concerned that Care Corner was owned by an out-of-town company. They just wanted to get back on their boards as quickly as possible.

---

[1] In contrast, Hood River Memorial Hospital struggled through the next decade and ultimately, in 1998, was purchased by the Providence Health System, after first rejecting an offer from MCMC. That same year, Scott moved the MCMC tenants out of Care Corner and sold the facility to Providence for a handsome profit.

In The Dalles, Scott began purchasing residences bordering the MCMC campus to ensure his hospital wasn't so landlocked that it couldn't accommodate future growth. He worked hard to forge tighter relationships with his medical staff to ensure their loyalty to MCMC and to strengthen his negotiating position with insurance companies. To reduce the odds that he would lose patients needing specialty care to Portland hospitals, Scott beefed up his visiting physician program and contracted with Portland-area providers to offer services that his population base couldn't support full time, such as cardiac care and medical oncology.

True to the spirit of MCMC's mission at the time, Scott was taking lots of names. He was winning the battle. His hospital was turning a profit while many others were bleeding red.

Scott's efforts weren't just focused inward. He used some of MCMC's profits to purchase, retrofit and staff a recreational vehicle, which he regularly sent out to the many tiny hamlets that surrounded The Dalles to perform preventive screenings and provide educational programs.

When the community swimming pool closed for lack of funds to make badly needed repairs, Scott pledged $100,000 from MCMC if voters passed a bond measure to cover the remaining costs. The measure passed by a mere 17 votes, but The Dalles Natatorium would soon become a source of tremendous community pride.

For all his success, however, Scott was beginning to grow weary of the battle mentality. In general, his relationship with his medical staff was good, but it seemed like at least one doctor was always mad at him. Despite his competitive nature, Scott loathed having to enter nursing contract negotiations, a time when professionals working on the same team and toward the same goals often became acrimonious opponents. After four years of regular and intense negotiations for insurance contracts, Scott was getting tired of being ground down.

And, though Scott had helped build a hospital that offered significantly more than most other rural healthcare facilities in Oregon, he still had an uneasy relationship with his community. Many residents of The Dalles viewed Scott's strategy of buying houses around the hospital as empire building. And when Scott took the initiative to get the community's swimming pool rebuilt, he heard grumbling that the hospital should stick to patient care and stay out of community affairs.

By 1989, just four years after Scott had taken over as MCMC's CEO, the thrill of competition was giving way to battle fatigue. He was disillusioned with the healthcare industry in general, and, despite his own hospital's successes, not particularly happy with the organization he had worked so hard to create.

Thoughts *from* Leland Kaiser

HOW DISCONTENT HELPS CREATE
A GREAT LEADER

Behind every great organization is a great leader, but how do great leaders come into being? What events or processes conspire to spur a leader to make a bold and high-risk attempt to transform an organization?

Leaders generally are thought to emerge in one of two ways. The first is that certain circumstances reach the critical point where someone stands up to the plate. A good example of this is Winston Churchill, who was uniquely stirred by the challenge of war and found his fulfillment in leading the democracies to victory. The second theory is that some leaders are simply born with inner qualities that predispose them to assume leadership roles.

I suspect there is also a third kind of leader — the person who emerges as a leader through a transformation process that leaves him or her very different from the person he or she was at the beginning. I suspect this is how Mark Scott evolved from a somewhat typical hospital administrator to a leader capable of completely transforming an organization and, in some respects, influencing an industry.

A profound, spiritual transforming process gives some people the motivation, desire, insight, or whatever it is, that changes their nature and propels them to greatness.

What sparks such a transformation? I believe there has to be some process of discontent. For many people, achieving success via the traditional business model is enough, and they are content to devote their entire careers to that pursuit. For other people, for whatever reason, this is not enough. At some point they realize, "I can't do this the rest of my life. It's not fulfilling me. I'm getting better and better at doing what I don't want to do."

People often call this "burnout," but it's not that. It's not that they *cannot* do the job anymore; it's that they don't *want* to do it anymore. It's not fun anymore. They are hungry and searching for something more. This discontent leaves them much more responsive to outside possibilities. They begin looking around and become more sensitive to ideas that are new and different. They suddenly see different messages, different insights, different world views and say, "I like that better than I like mine."

Most people don't fight their environment; they just adapt to it. They can adapt themselves out of existence before they'll challenge their environment. But some people will eventually say, "I don't want to be a passive adapter; I want to become the center of action. Rather than having the environment act upon me, I will act upon the environment."

Of course, that creates a real reversal of dynamics. Suddenly, that person becomes a disruptive force. He or she is rocking the boat and changing the chemistry of everything. If that person is in a leadership position, his or her people will have to change the way they are to match the way their leader has changed.

Mark Scott was tired of his environment, tired of doing what everyone else in healthcare was doing. He was doing it successfully and could have continued doing it that way until he retired. But that wasn't enough for him. He was ready to leave. In the next chapter, you'll see how a chance meeting at a healthcare conference was the spark that ignited a profound spiritual transformation in Mark, which ultimately would spark profound organizational transformation at Mid-Columbia Medical Center.

Discontent may have been the driving factor behind Mark's transformation, but what else produces the spark of personal transformation? I believe that whenever a person exhibits signs of anxiety, unrest and changes in energy level, he or she is being staged and getting ready for change. This is often viewed the wrong way, as a psychiatric problem. The person is seen as someone who can't stand the heat and needs to get out of the kitchen.

Rather than viewing this as something being wrong, we should see it as something being right. Those symptoms can be used as fuel to spur personal growth.

For a true transformation to occur, a leader must be driven by principles rather than personal security. Because invariably a leader will get to the point of drawing a line in the sand and saying, "This is what I need to do. If the rest of you don't want to do it, that's okay; but if that's the case, I'm moving on."

There may come a time when you have to ask yourself, "Is this decision worth my career?" If the answer is "No," then you step back. But every once in a while, the answer is "Yes."

CHAPTER 2

EPIPHANY

In his first four years as CEO, Mark Scott spent considerable effort improving the care and service that patients, visitors and others experienced at Mid-Columbia Medical Center.

Melding his own management beliefs and style with the theories and writings of others, Scott designed a series of quality-improvement and customer-service initiatives. Tom Peters was a favorite of Scott's, and he often refashioned memorable passages from the management guru's best-selling book, *In Search of Excellence*, into rallying cries for his own team members. ("You may start a patient's heart beating again or send his cancer into remission, but if he has to sleep with a lumpy pillow, that may be the first thing he remembers about his stay at Mid-Columbia Medical Center.")

In the spring of 1989, Scott traveled with his board chairman, Terry Cochran, to a Peters-led conference in Pajaro Dunes, California. After one particularly long day of breakout sessions, Scott returned to his hotel room for a few minutes of rest before a dinner program. A room-service meal and a quiet evening with a book sounded much more appealing to him than the grip-and-grin social that was part of the dinner conference program. Scott had never heard of the evening's keynote speaker or the program she directed and would be presenting. He knew, though, that he could not abandon his board chairman. So, Scott changed his clothes and reluctantly headed to the event, little knowing that it would change the course of his career and the future of healthcare in his community.

After dinner, the featured speaker, a woman named Robin Orr, began telling the story of a program she directed called Planetree. This was the point in the evening when Scott had assumed he would be fighting back yawns. Instead, he became transfixed as Orr spoke of the program she described as the result of "one determined woman's commitment to creating a bold new model in hospital care."

Orr explained that the determined woman behind Planetree was Angelica Thieriot. The Argentine-born wife of a prominent San Francisco businessman, Thieriot was hospitalized for several weeks in 1977 for treatment of a mysterious virus. It was Thieriot's first experience in an American hospital, and, though impressed by the hospital's technological capabilities, she was appalled by the impersonal care she received.

Thieriot spent many hours staring at the bare walls of her room. Staff hurried in and out, rarely explaining what they were doing to her or why, let alone conversing with her on a personal level. Adhering to strict visiting hours, staff took great pains to limit Thieriot's interactions with family members and friends. Sick with a mysterious illness that no one could diagnose or explain to her, Thieriot was scared, lonely and bored.

Despite the technological advantages of the American hospital, Thieriot was far more impressed with the care she had received in the Argentine hospital where she had delivered her two sons. There, she was tended to by a single nurse who knew her by name and treated her as a human being, rather than just a body in a bed that needed its vital signs checked. Staff answered her questions. Family members and friends were welcome at all times. The Argentine hospital may have been technologically inferior to the American one, but it was infinitely more humane.

Soon after her discharge from the American hospital,[2] Thieriot turned her attention to finding a way to integrate the technological capabilities of the modern hospital with a more spiritual dimension. Her vision was to create a healing setting in which values such as compassion, comfort, aesthetics, dignity, shared knowledge and informed choice shared equal billing with technology.

[2] Thieriot's illness was never diagnosed, but she made a complete recovery.

Given the nature of the typical American hospital in the 1970s, the concept seemed revolutionary. In reality, it was not even particularly original. More than 2,000 years earlier, the Greek physician, Hippocrates, had founded modern medicine on a similar set of beliefs.

Thieriot formed a group of advisers to help develop components of the program she named Planetree, after the sycamore tree under which Hippocrates was said to have taught the healing arts to his students. In 1978, the group found a willing partner in California Pacific (then Pacific Presbyterian) Medical Center, a 272-bed tertiary-care hospital in San Francisco.

Three years later, the first element of the program came to life when the Planetree Health Resource Center opened on the California Pacific campus. The freestanding center housed hundreds of medical texts, news clippings and other health-related educational materials available to the public at no charge.

In 1985, the first patients were admitted to a Planetree inpatient wing at California Pacific. The 13-bed unit had been meticulously remodeled to create an environment that program proponents believed would be more conducive to healing than the traditional American hospital setting, which had not changed significantly in decades.

The hallway's stark walls, bright overhead lighting and cold linoleum were replaced with tasteful wallpaper, soft track lighting and carpeting. Warm wood features were used generously throughout the unit and patient rooms, in cabinetry, window casings and elsewhere.

The Planetree unit included a kitchen and private dining area, so patients and family members could snack any time of the day or night, or even fix their own meals if they desired. A dietitian was available to teach healthy eating and provide recipes.

Visiting hours were abolished to help alleviate the fear and sense of isolation often brought on by hospitalization. Loved ones were welcome to stay overnight in the patient rooms, which resembled cozy hotel suites.

Room numbers were hand-painted on ceramic tiles. Patients slept under floral sheets and bedspreads, and looked up at bookshelves they could personalize with photos, cards, flowers and other belongings. Each room had VCR and audiotape players, and patients could select movies and music from an extensive library.

A massage therapist was available to soothe aching muscles. A resident storyteller was even on hand to help take patients' minds off their medical concerns.

The Planetree environment turned the traditional hospital design upside down because every feature was approached from the standpoint of how it would best meet the needs of the patient. Not the physician. Not the nurse. Not the administrator.

As Orr continued to outline the details of this innovative approach to patient care, Scott thought to himself: "Gee, putting the patient first. How revolutionary."

Scott learned that the approach Planetree prescribed for the hospital environment was only one part of the equation, and not even the most important part. "That", Orr said, "was the effort Planetree made to encourage patients to become more active participants in their own care."

Each patient admitted to the Planetree unit was asked to choose a care partner — a family member or friend who would work closely with the patient and health professionals during the hospitalization. The care partner was taught to deliver medications, change dressings and perform other procedures that would ease the patient's transition to his or her home after discharge.

At the core of the Planetree philosophy was the belief that every patient had the basic right of unfettered access to information about his or her illness and the manner in which it was being treated. Where hospitals traditionally had kept patients' medical records shrouded in secrecy and out of the reach of everyone but doctors and nurses, Planetree brought them out into the open and encouraged patients to read their own records. They were, after all, *their* medical records. And, if patients were motivated to learn all they could about their condition, who would want to deny them that opportunity?

Planetree patients also were urged, if they wished, to learn about their conditions and be true partners in their care. Each patient had the opportunity to receive a detailed packet of consumer-friendly health information, prepared by the Planetree Health Resource Center staff.

Patients who were curious about a particular nontraditional, complementary therapy found support from the Planetree staff, an unlikely possibility in most other hospitals.

Planetree employed the primary nursing model, in which each patient was assigned a primary nurse who coordinated his or her care throughout the hospital stay. Like the care Angelica Thieriot had experienced at home in Argentina, the approach helped deepen the bond between the caregivers and their patients.

Orr's enthusiasm for this brave new concept in patient care was palpable. Her talk was liberally sprinkled with words Scott never had heard in his years in the hospital industry. Planetree had adopted a mantra that caught Scott's attention when Orr recited it: "We're trying to personalize, humanize and demystify the hospital experience for patients," she told the audience. And Orr used other words that Scott could not remember ever hearing a hospital CEO utter, including himself — words like honesty, respect and dignity.

As Orr brought her story of Planetree to closure, Scott thought of his own hospital. The vision that came to him was that of a patient walking down a hallway cluttered with medication carts, gurneys and food trays. With one hand, the patient pushed an IV pole. With the other, he clutched the back of his flimsy hospital gown, trying to keep it closed. Scott had come across the scene dozens of times in his own hospital — a patient, a human being, in an unfamiliar setting, alone and surrounded by unfamiliar people, trying to salvage some semblance of dignity.

Before this dinner meeting, Scott had thought of MCMC as an outstanding hospital, as good as any other rural hospital its size. Maybe better than most. Certainly it was a hospital to be proud of. MCMC had a diverse and talented medical staff, compassionate nurses and other caregivers, and a solid management team. Scott had been adding technology, as he could, that was appropriate for his service area. The physical plant was showing signs of age, but a remodeling of the patient units was on the drawing board.

Now, suddenly and almost painfully, Scott realized what his hospital was missing most — a soul. No meaningful values guided the activities of Scott and his employees. In his struggle for market share, his intense negotiations with insurers, his skirmishes with physicians and his dogged pursuit of a positive bottom line, Scott had lost sight of MCMC's raison d'être: to help patients heal as quickly, as completely and as humanely as possible.

"It occurred to me that my hospital — the traditional hospital — was just like a jail," Scott said. "We signed you in, took away your identity, gave you a wrist tag, stripped you of all your personal possessions, threw you into a sterile room, gave you a ridiculous gown that exposed your backside, fed you bad food, told you when you could and couldn't have visitors, woke you up at all hours of the night to poke needles into you or make you swallow pills and rarely talked to you, let alone told you what we were doing to you and why. We were terrible to people, really, and we always had been. But it wasn't until I heard Robin speak that it became obvious to me."

As Orr closed her comments, she spoke of Planetree's plans for expanding into other settings. A second, 25-bed model unit would be opening at San Jose Medical Center during the next year, 1990. Planetree also hoped to implement model units in a few other select settings, including a small, rural hospital and a large, inner-city hospital on the East Coast. But Orr, Planetree's executive director, revealed that the organization had an even greater aspiration.

"One day," she said, "I'll find a CEO with enough guts to implement this program throughout an entire hospital."

As Orr finished, Scott poked his elbow into the ribcage of Cochran, his board chairman, who was seated next to him. "I think she's talking about us," Scott said.

True to his nature, Mark Scott latched onto Planetree with clenched-tooth determination. He cornered Orr after her talk, telling her, "That CEO you were looking for to implement Planetree hospital-wide? That's me, and Mid-Columbia Medical Center is your hospital." Then Scott returned to The Dalles and set about the task of selling the concept to his key constituencies — his board, his 75-member medical staff, his nurses and his employees.

Though Scott knew the dramatic changes brought by the implementation of Planetree — architectural and otherwise — would create a stir in the conservative Mid-Columbia region, he wasn't concerned about long-term, negative public reaction. He never considered conducting a community survey to measure receptiveness to the Planetree conversion, as many leaders might have done before launching such a bold initiative.

First, he believed fervently that implementing Planetree was simply the right thing to do. Second, he was confident that all he had to do to convert a skeptic was to get him or her, or a friend or loved one, into his hospital once Planetree was in place. Then, Scott believed, Planetree could sell itself. Finally, Scott planned to offer Planetree's concepts and programs to patients as a choice, not a requirement. If they preferred care the "old-fashioned way," they would be able to receive it that way.

Scott wasn't sure what to expect from his other audiences. But whatever their reaction, he had no intention of just testing the waters with a few elements of Planetree. He wanted to land a backward, three-and-a-half somersault, full-gainer from the high platform, and if he caused a few ripples, so be it. Scott loved metaphors and stories, and at this moment, he was reminded of a story he had heard from Armand Shapiro, who ran a Houston company called Garden Ridge Pottery:

"He was talking about how he was having trouble getting his employees to support his attempt to expand the company's product line," Scott said. "He was bound and determined to get this done, with or without them, and so he told them, 'This train is going to Chicago. If you want to go to Topeka, that's okay. But you need to know you're on the wrong train, and you need to get off.' Planetree was my Chicago."

Scott already had made up his mind — either MCMC was going Planetree, or he was going somewhere else. As much as he was taken with the Planetree concept, Scott was equally impressed with, and envious of, Robin Orr's almost evangelical passion for her work. Somewhere along the way, Scott had lost his passion.

"As a hospital CEO or any kind of leader, you make dozens of critical decisions every day," he said. "But very few of them are worth your career. This one was. I wanted to feel the same way Robin did about healthcare, and I was a long way from that."

Scott had talked with his wife, Jacque, who was also MCMC's director of nursing, and they had decided that they were prepared to leave the community if Scott didn't get the support to implement Planetree.

"If I couldn't do Planetree, I was ready to start my OR consulting business," Scott said. "I was just an angry CEO, and in Planetree I saw my salvation. I knew this was the way we should be treating patients. Mid-Columbia was a good hospital, but now we needed to give attention to our core values."

Determined as he was, Scott also was optimistic that he already had the components in place to create a total Planetree environment — from his laundry room to his boardroom. The CEO always had benefited from the support and guidance of a progressive and stable board of directors. His relationship with his medical staff was on solid ground, and, anyway, he knew as long as his board was behind him, he would have the clout to overcome any serious challenges from physicians. Jacque Scott was universally respected as a leader of the MCMC nurses, and certainly that would work in his favor as he attempted to change almost completely the manner in which they were practicing.

Although he had plenty of faith in his other employees, Scott felt they might prove to be his toughest sell, if only because of the logistical difficulty of communicating to all 600 of them the depth of his conviction to the Planetree conversion — and the critical role each of them played in the program's success.

Other factors could work in favor of the Planetree conversion. In a difficult healthcare environment, MCMC wasn't flush with cash, but it had remained profitable in the face of significant challenges. And, with a renovation project already planned and budgeted for, the timing could not have been better to begin creating the physical component of the Planetree model.

While selling Planetree to doctors and nurses would be a challenging exercise — asking them to make, in some instances, significant sacrifices for the benefit of their patients — he knew he could approach his board on a couple of fronts. The primary one was that Scott believed Planetree would appeal to board members for the same reason it appealed to him: Simply, this was the way people should be cared for. But he also knew that Planetree could appeal to the board's sense of fiscal responsibility.

In the new healthcare environment, in which hospitals were being reimbursed by predetermined (or capitated) rates based on a patient's diagnosis, the shorter the patient's stay, the greater the hospital's chance of making money. One result was that patients weren't being admitted until their conditions were more serious, and they were often discharged sooner than they would have been in the past.

Scott was able to make a strong case that, by having 100-percent R.N. staffing and giving nurses total care responsibilities; by providing patients with information about their illnesses and treatment alternatives; and by involving family members in the care process, both patients and MCMC would be better off. He could reduce MCMC patients' average length of stay, send them and their family member home better prepared to provide their own follow-up care, and reduce expensive readmissions from complications.

Yes, the remodeling project would now be more expensive, and the price tag to retrain 600 employees and implement a new nursing model was sure to be significant. But over the long-term, Scott reasoned, MCMC might pay an even steeper price for *not* implementing Planetree.

Scott's first step was to develop a core group of key supporters, starting with respected board members and physicians. Though Scott was already sounding like the Planetree program's unofficial public relations director (so immersed was Scott in the Planetree philosophy that his managers were counting the number of times he used the words "personalize," "humanize" and "demystify" in a single conversation), he knew that his enthusiasm could only carry his pitch so far. By fall 1989, Scott was ready to take a small group of physicians, staff and board members with him to visit the Planetree unit at Pacific Presbyterian Medical Center in San Francisco.

"I knew once they saw and felt Planetree in action, they'd get it," Scott said.

Robert Staver, M.D., an orthopedic surgeon and MCMC board member, made that first trip. "From the moment I heard about

Planetree, I was really intrigued because it spoke to a lot of things that were important to me as a physician," Staver said. "When we visited the unit in San Francisco, it was filled primarily with AIDS patients. I remember thinking how comfortable and non-threatening the environment was — how could a patient not feel better in this kind of a setting?

"Patients were watching videos, and the staff talked about how they tried to incorporate humor as much as possible into their patients' stays. That struck a note with me, because I had always used humor a lot in my practice. It helped break down barriers and, I felt, allowed me to communicate better with my patients."

Staver was a lover of music and the arts (his wife, Janice, is both a musician and a painter), and Planetree's incorporation of the healing arts into traditional medicine made perfect sense to him.

"You saw the beautiful paintings in the unit, and you heard the music playing in the hallways. Maybe the patients were in a condition to appreciate it, and maybe they weren't," Staver said. "But the staff always could, and I always believe that what you do for yourself, you also do for your patients. If you're a doctor or nurse in the middle of a hectic day and you have something that gives you more of a sense of peace, your patients are going to benefit from that. So, I felt from the start that the benefits of Planetree extended beyond patients and their families."

If, after his experience in the inpatient unit at Pacific Presbyterian, Staver wasn't already convinced he wanted to see Planetree at MCMC, his visit to Pacific's Planetree Health Resource Center would have sealed the deal.

"I struck up a conversation with a woman whose husband was scheduled to have orthopedic surgery," he remembered. "I looked around and quickly found a good book that I knew described the procedure in terms the layperson could understand. I took this woman through the book a little bit, and then she sat down at a table and started learning about what her husband would soon be going through. I had always believed it was important to have opportunities to be enlightened and informed, and that was something that had been missing in healthcare. And there I was, in this special place, devoted exclusively to that."

Staver and his fellow board members (including board chairman Terry Cochran, who was witness to Scott's epiphany in Pajaro Dunes) were easy converts. "I was blessed to have a board with a rare mixture of vision and energy," Scott said. "They just got it."

As it happened, MCMC's physicians got it, too. Scott anticipated that his medical staff might be leery of what he was trying to accomplish, but he was happily surprised when he met few obstacles. In his tenure as CEO, Scott had taken great pains to strengthen the ties between the physicians and the hospital.

Whenever feasible and appropriate, Scott heeded physician requests to add new technology and services at MCMC. He supported, with both dollars and staff expertise, their efforts to market their practices. On one memorable occasion, Scott had fax machines delivered to every physician's office to help them order tests more easily and communicate more efficiently with hospital departments. Like all hospital CEOs, Scott had his share of skirmishes with physicians, but few had left scars.

Scott's efforts to bring the physicians on board also benefited from a recent string of retirements that had seen several longtime physicians replaced with younger doctors who were more amenable to change.

"If Mark had tried a few years earlier, Planetree never would have happened," said Bill Hamilton, M.D., a surgeon and a key Planetree supporter from the start.

"There were several physicians on the staff then who, no matter what you put on their plate, weren't going to eat it," Hamilton said. "You would never have gotten those guys to sit down with a patient and say, 'These are your choices; it's up to you and your family to decide what we're going to do.' Their attitude was, 'You came to me because you thought I knew what was best for you. So listen to me tell you what's best for you.' But we had experienced an influx of new doctors who were much more open and sensitive to new ideas."

Scott held a series of meetings with medical staff members, making sure he had a strong physician supporter like Staver or Hamilton in attendance at each one. He assumed that Planetree's policy of open medical records was going to raise some eyebrows, but once again, he had prepared for a fight that never really materialized.

"Many of us felt uncomfortable at first about patients having access to their medical records," Staver recalled. "But nobody could come up with a particularly compelling argument for why a record shouldn't be open. The idea just fell out of our comfort zone."

Added Hamilton: "I think most physicians' main concern was that opening the medical record was going to take more of their time because now they were going to have to write more legibly. But I also had conversations with several doctors who would say, 'Patients don't have the right to look at my chart.' And I'd have to say to them, 'Wait a minute; whose chart is it, anyway?'"[3]

To a few MCMC physicians, the specter of seeing patients who were actually informed about their medical conditions or, worse, their treatment options, was much more troublesome than having to mind their penmanship. Physicians already were woefully short on time; the last thing they needed, they argued, was to spend an hour discussing the merits of a new-age treatment their patient had read about.

But Planetree was, above all else, about choice and patient rights. And, for Scott, the patients' right to information — and the physicians' obligation to help their patients sift out the good information from the bad — was nonnegotiable.

"Without seeing Planetree in action, the whole concept did sound a little touchy-feely," Hamilton said. "And so, physicians were saying, 'What is this anyway, a hospital or a spa?'

"They were worried that Mark and the administration would lose their focus and that money would be spent on touchy-feely stuff instead of things that were 'really important.' But those physicians represented a significant minority. And once Planetree was implemented, that kind of grousing just went away."

Scott relied in part on the MCMC board to help him get the message across to the physicians that the hospital's future lay with Planetree and the doctors needed to embrace the program.

[3]In the years after Planetree was implemented, about one-third of MCMC patients closely reviewed their records. Another third were curious but trusted their physicians implicitly and didn't bother, and the remaining patients were too ill.

"My philosophy was that the board of directors grants physicians the right to practice at this hospital," Scott said. "It is not a physician's ordained right. So the bottom line was, we had the authority to say, 'When you come into this hospital, you leave your ego at the door.' That was critical, because in the Planetree way of thinking, there is no role for the egomaniac."

If Scott was pleasantly surprised by his medical staff's general acceptance of Planetree, his nurses' negative response caught him completely off guard. As Scott saw it, if he was an evangelist preaching the gospel of Planetree throughout MCMC, his nursing staff would be his choir, laying down a harmonious backing track all the way through the process. In Scott's mind, Planetree offered the opportunity to practice what he called "perfect nursing."

But many of his nurses weren't buying in. Not even after Scott offered umpteen workshops and numerous offsite retreats. Not even after he had Robin Orr come to MCMC and speak about Planetree. Not even after he arranged several additional site visits with nurses to Pacific Presbyterian. Scott was at his wit's end.

"They didn't understand it, didn't trust that it could happen or weren't committed to providing total patient care," Scott said. "They were nervous about physician response and the idea that families would be brought into the care process. And many of them just didn't get it."

Tia Bailey was one of the hard sells. "I was new to MCMC, so I didn't really know Mark or the hospital board," Bailey said. "All I knew was that I had been in nursing for 15 years and had never seen a hospital board committed to anything besides the bottom line. I had come to fully accept that, as long as I was a good employee and practiced well, that was all that mattered, and I was going to be okay. Until I saw that commitment from the MCMC board and from Mark, I was like, 'Leave me alone and let me take care of my patients.'"

Nurse Roberta Carson loved what she heard about Planetree and wanted to believe Scott when he said his commitment was for real. But she also had spent a lot of time at other hospitals where promises were made — and broken.

"A lot of us were wondering if Planetree was just Mark's flavor of the day," Carson said. "It sounded good, but we had this fear that it was not going to last."

At offsite retreats, nurses were given the opportunity to be integrally involved in the design and implementation of Planetree at MCMC from the ground up. Nurses were encouraged to provide input on everything from the design of the nursing stations and units to the clothing they would wear on the floor. In one exercise, they were asked to close their eyes and visualize the perfect nursing job. One after another, they would describe a job that sounded very much like that of a Planetree nurse.

And still, Scott sensed, many of the nurses did not believe Planetree could be pulled off at MCMC — or worse, that Scott would not see it through to its completion.

Finally, Scott had had enough. At home, Scott had shared with Jacque his concerns about her staff, but now he was going directly to the nurses themselves. At yet another nursing meeting, Scott stood up and addressed those in attendance: "Damn it, you just don't get it," he railed. "And you're going to get it, if it takes sending every last one of you down to San Francisco to see Planetree for yourself."

By the time Planetree was implemented at MCMC, Scott would send nearly three-quarters of his nursing staff on site visits to the Planetree units in San Francisco and San Jose. That was another huge investment, but it paid off.

"I didn't understand that each nurse needed to see, touch, feel, smell and hear what a soulful healthcare experience could be like," Scott said. "They needed to experience it the same way I had. Taking the nurses to Planetree was the most important decision I made."

"That made all the difference to me," Carson said. "After seeing Planetree, we were all asking, 'Why haven't we been doing this all along?'"

The train had left the station, with almost everyone at MCMC on board.

Thoughts *from* Leland Kaiser

HOW A CEO BECOMES AN EDGE RUNNER

In my opinion, Mark Scott was, and is, a classic edge runner. Edge runners share certain common characteristics. My observations of Mark confirm that he demonstrates most of these characteristics.

Introducing the Edge Runner

I believe we are living on the edge between two eras, two cultural mindsets and two very different ways of doing things. We are an in-between generation caught between an old way of thinking and a new way of perceiving our world. We are living on the edge between two surfaces. (Visualize where the surface on a tabletop meets the side.)

We are a transition generation. We lived through the last years of an old century and are now living in the early years of our new century. We are approaching a tremendous expansion of planetary consciousness. The world is ripe for our efforts.

Edges have fascinating possibilities. However, not all people love them. Some people approach the edge, become fearful and retreat to the safety of an old and familiar surface. Other people get reckless and fall off the edge into despair and ruin. A few brave travelers, the edge runners, use the edge as a launch platform to leap into new possibilities. These travelers, like Mark Scott, are the way-makers for our new world. They lay down the pathway for others to follow.

The edge leads to an expanding multiverse. On the edge you will experience an acceleration of time and space. You will experience an identity crisis. You are no longer the old and not yet the new. You are on an interstice. You will sense endless possibilities as your psychic energy, previously bound in old patterns, is freed to assume new forms.

On the edge, your creative imagination can be used to redefine reality. You will experience the thrill of birthing new worlds. To travel on the edge, you must confront your fears and prepare to move into hyperspace. You must learn to trust the process of change. You are an initiate of a new era of humankind. It takes a particular psychology to thrive on the edge.

On the edge, we view circumstances as neutral, and we supply the spin. Everything happening in the world is viewed as one single event. Synchronicity is an outcome of this singularity. The edge-state traveler acts upon all opportunities that synchronicity brings. On the edge, you take responsibility for creating your preferred reality. You understand that the universe will support you 100 percent. You embrace chaos as unlimited opportunity. No longer are you determined by your past. You have entered a new surface of your being. You must open your consciousness to radical new possibilities. Your imagination becomes the tool of creation. You are as limited as it is, but no more so.

Mark Scott is an edge runner. This explains much of his success at MCMC. I believe he had a natural aptitude for edge running, but most of his insight and skill was gained on the job doing the work of a CEO.

Why don't all CEOs become edge runners? I don't know. I suppose like everything else, a special combination of genetic aptitude and environmental opportunity are necessary. But there is also the issue of moral choice. Mark chose to become the person he is now. He could have chosen otherwise. His life would have been easier, but not nearly as notable.

CHAPTER 3

An Environment for Healing

"The early church created the first monastic infirmaries, providing care for the sick and the poor. The design of these Christian infirmaries resembled churches or cathedrals of healing. Patients were housed in large, open wards, which faced an elevated chapel brilliantly illuminated by stained-glass windows. As they lay in their beds, the patients could look up into the soaring vaulted ceilings, which were flooded with celestial light from the windows above... The hospital of the future will rediscover the power and effectiveness of therapeutic design, improving the quality of the workplace for its staff and the quality of care for its patients. The hospital can again become a temple, promoting and assisting the healing process."

– Donald C. McKahan
Healing Healthcare

"The experience of my mother's death began with a phone call telling me to get home as quickly as I could. At 1 a.m., after a long, unexpected flight, I stepped off the elevators of the hospital where she was and into a very large waiting room, harshly lit with overhead fluorescent lights, off-white walls, and a white and green tile floor. The only chairs were orange vinyl and chrome, and they all were hooked together by their arms. There was nothing else at

all in the area to welcome a visitor. On the back of one of the
chairs was a handwritten sign telling visitors, 'Don't sleep here.'
My first thought was that I wasn't welcome to be a part of my
mom's care. It was clear they didn't want me to hang around here.
I knew I was a long way from my own hospital."

– Tia Bailey, R.N.
Mid-Columbia Medical Center

Before 1991, the ambiance of Mid-Columbia Medical Center was not unlike most other hospitals of the time — or bowling alleys, for that matter.

The facility had undergone its last major remodeling project in the mid-1970s, and the telltale signs of that era were present everywhere — in the bright, fluorescent overhead lighting; in the gray metal desks and orange fabric cubicles that comprised the nursing stations; and in the bold, geometric graphics that zigged and zagged up and down the walls of the hospital corridors like psychedelic electrocardiograms.

Patient rooms were what patient rooms had always been — white walls, supermarket-style linoleum floors and battleship-gray, stainless-steel furnishings. The hospital's few waiting areas were equally clinical and unimaginative. Designed for heavy traffic and easy upkeep, they all but screamed, "Don't get too comfortable here."

A few decades earlier, as the original plans were being drawn for The Dalles' new hospital, some designer no doubt had paid particular attention to making the physical plant as functional, convenient and utilitarian as possible — for physicians, nurses, dietary staff, housekeepers, maintenance staff and other hospital personnel. Each successive remodel had built on that same design philosophy.

In 1991, traveling from one end of an MCMC patient unit to the other typically required slaloming around all manner of hospital apparatus — gurneys, medication carts, laundry bags, IV poles, dietary trays, mop buckets and the like. During the trip, travelers could find out if anyone they knew had been admitted, since each patient's name was written on the large grease board in the middle of the hall, conveniently posted for staff — and all other interested parties — to see.

The hospital's 1970s remodeling had been undertaken partly to accommodate MCMC's transition to a modular nursing model. That was an attempt to increase efficiencies by moving nurses closer to their patients. But, of course, not *too* close.

Designers made sure to plant sufficient obstacles between the nurses and those in their care. For example, with tall modular walls lining its perimeter, the nursing station remained a clearly defined fortress. A patient would have to be quite sick, or a visitor rather thick, not to understand that this area was strictly off-limits.

For more than a decade, Mark Scott had worked in this environment without giving it a second thought. He had worked in hospitals his entire professional life, for that matter, and MCMC matched the expected norm. This is what hospitals looked like. Sure, by now many had begun sprucing up their birthing units to create a homier environment in which to welcome a newborn. But the prevailing thought was that mothers weren't really patients; they weren't even sick. They were there by choice. Mothers usually were healthy, conscious and insured.

The birthing process presented the hospital with the opportunity to create that all-important, positive first impression with people who might later need other hospital services. In the birthing center, a hospital could set the hook that might catch a customer for life. It only made sense to treat these people differently from the unfortunate patients who occupied other areas of the facility.

Scott had agreed with this mindset, right up to the moment he heard Planetree's Robin Orr describe the ideal hospital setting. Now, he was on a mission to ensure that every person who walked into MCMC — patient, visitor, employee, vendor or otherwise — would have a memorable, positive experience. And that meant changing everything in the organization, from the ground up.

So it was that, as nursing training continued and a curriculum was being developed for the ambitious orientation program through which every one of MCMC's 600 employees would pass, the walls came tumbling down at the hospital.

In spring 1991, MCMC's medical and surgical units, which occupied the top two of the hospital's four floors, were virtually gutted. Over the next several months, a traditional American hospital would be dramatically transformed into a place that, in the eyes of Scott and other Planetree believers, better promoted healing, learning and patient participation.

MCMC's nurses had been intimately involved in the design of the new patient care areas. Nearly three-quarters of the nursing staff had been able to visit the Planetree unit at Pacific Presbyterian and a second model unit that had opened at San Jose Medical Center in 1990. Though not all had seen Planetree in action, *every* MCMC nurse was afforded the opportunity to provide input on what the ideal hospital should look like.

Eric Rigenhagen, a young associate from Kimberly Bragg Interior Design of San Francisco, worked closely with Jacque Scott, nursing director, to ensure that the new MCMC was not only beautiful, but also functional for the nurses and other staff. "Jacque would walk me through every department and tell me the tasks that each nurse would perform in each space — how they worked, where they usually stood, the equipment they used and would need easy access to. We would draw up preliminary designs for the spaces and then interview the nurses to make sure we were adequately addressing their needs," Rigenhagen said.

Joyce Powell-Morin, R.N., who took over as vice president of nursing in 1999 after Jacque Scott left MCMC to become a private consultant, said the nurses continued to be involved throughout the design process.

"We went through every component of the remodeling with our nurses and explored every option," she said. "They got to provide their opinions on the nurses' stations, the bathrooms, the sinks, the patient closets, everything."

Holding the nursing retreats, setting up site visits and seeking input in the design process helped Scott and his managers secure the nurses' buy-in, without which Planetree at MCMC could not have succeeded. Said nurse Tia Bailey: "The decision to become a Planetree hospital was made without my input, but because I was included in so much after the decision was made, I felt valued. That was very important to me."

Involving the nurses so intimately in the process also helped ensure that, although the new units would be designed to best accommodate the patients' needs, they would still be practical for the caregivers.

By April 1992, the breathtaking transformation of MCMC was ready to be unveiled. That MCMC was now a hospital of an entirely new breed was apparent from the moment a visitor entered the building. The main entrance opened into a large waiting area that could have been the subject of a spread in *Traditional Home* magazine. Large, comfortable sofas and wingback chairs, upholstered in rich floral and striped fabrics, were arranged around mahogany coffee tables. The room was bathed in soft light emanating from rustic brass table and floor lamps. Original paintings from local artists and wallpaper adorned the walls, and fabric window treatments completed the welcoming atmosphere.

Visitors entering through the rear of the hospital walked through revolving doors into a magnificent four-story, glass atrium with terracotta tiled floors, a baby grand piano and a towering fern-covered rock waterfall.

Even the elevators to MCMC's patient units had been accessorized with tartan wallpaper and oak wainscoting. When the doors opened on the third and fourth floors, they revealed long, carpeted nursing corridors, leading to large windows that framed breathtaking views of the rolling hills across the Columbia River. Here, too, wallpaper, oak railings and original artwork of Columbia Gorge scenes erased any memories of the bold, graphic stripes that once burdened these same walls. Lighting was soft and indirect. Overhead fixtures were frosted to eliminate the blinding glare that used to punish patients who kept their eyes open as they traveled through the halls on gurneys.

Perhaps the most visible sign of change in MCMC's patient units was what *wasn't* visible in the hallways: clutter. In fact, anyone who cluttered the hallways with apparatus did so at the risk of incurring Scott's wrath.

"The units were designed with places to stow all the equipment that used to be in the hallways," Scott said. "The goal was to never leave anything sitting out. Those hallways were where patients would take the first steps toward reclaiming their lives after they'd had surgery or a debilitating medical condition. They'd been sick and bedridden, and I wanted the first 10 or 15 steps they took after that to be sacred. That meant they weren't going to be having to serpent around a bunch of clutter."

At the end of the nursing corridors nearest to the elevators, patient and family activity rooms (Planetree's version of a waiting room) opened onto the atrium and to the soothing, natural sounds of the waterfall below. Comfortable furniture, a television, a writing desk, a telephone, a game table, a saltwater aquarium and shelves full of books and periodicals welcomed visitors and encouraged them to stay for as long as they liked.

Across the hallway, a full galley kitchen and dining room were available for patients and family members. Down the corridor, a large library was stocked with health-related books, magazines and videotapes in lay language. At the end of each floor farthest from the elevators, looking out onto the neighborhood below, and the river and hills beyond it, quiet lounges offered patients and visitors sanctuary.

Said Scott: "When we designed the units, we specifically identified areas, besides the patient rooms, that were to be considered safe havens for patients and family members. They were the activity room, the kitchen-dining room, the quiet lounge and the library. We wanted to create spaces where people could be alone or with their family in private; or where a physician could discuss confidential information with a family member or colleague."

The nursing stations on each floor — which had so recently resembled fortresses — now featured a wide-open floor plan designed to encourage interaction between patients and their caregivers. The stations also featured more homelike furnishings, such as heavy walnut tables that served as workstations.

The sterile patient rooms of MCMC's past had been converted into comfortable havens for healing. Cold stainless steel was replaced wherever possible with warm wood. The commercial blinds that once covered the large windows in each patient room were replaced with soft curtains.

Floor coverings (including attractive vinyl tiles and wood laminate), color schemes, wallpaper and window treatments varied from room to room, eliminating the "sameness" of design that hospital planners over the years had perpetuated, as if it were a requirement.

"We wanted each room to be unique," said Rigenhagen, the designer. "So, although we had a cohesive color scheme, we very rarely re-used the same fabric and materials from one room to the next."[4]

Each room was equipped with a TV/VCR and a comfortable sleeper chair to accommodate overnight visitors. Shelving and bulletin boards were available to help patients personalize their rooms with photos, cards or other items from home. Patients could even choose the paintings that would adorn their walls throughout their stay, selecting from an art cart that was wheeled into their room shortly after they were admitted.

Adjustable lighting cut the harshness of overhead fluorescents and enabled nurses to check on patients in the middle of the night without waking them. And, whenever practical, technology and other clinical necessities were tucked away in attractive wood cabinetry.

Reinventing the look of a hospital was a first for Rigenhagen, who had only been designing for two years and had no experience outside the residential setting. "I think that was actually a good thing," he said. "A designer with experience in the hospital setting might have been pre-programmed for what it should look like and have difficulty making the adjustments that this environment demanded. I just didn't see any limitations, because I didn't know better. For example, I had no preconceived notion of what a patient room should look like. I just saw a bedroom."

Considering that so much of Rigenhagen's furnishings required custom manufacturing, few would have guessed that his portion of the project would actually come in under budget.

---

[4] To help ensure the bedspreads and other furnishings were returned to the right room after laundering, Rigenhagen tagged each item with the correct room number and even developed what he called an "owner's manual," a detailed inventory of every bedspread, lamp and pillow, and its correct placement in the hospital. "We wanted to make sure that long after we were gone, someone would be able to go back and easily recreate the entire setting if the need arose," he said.

"We were working with what would have been considered a fairly standard design budget for a typical hospital project," Rigenhagen said. "We came up with a figure for how much we would have to spend in each room or area. Then we started going to manufacturers and saying things like, 'We need a simple brass pull that a patient with only one functioning finger can easily use. Can you make this quantity for this much?' Because we were ordering such large quantities, we were very successful in finding manufacturers wanting to work with us."

For example, Rigenhagen found a single company in Texas that made many of the custom furnishings designed for the patient rooms, such as oak headboards and bedside tables, sleeper beds and patient chairs. In concert with Jacque Scott, Rigenhagen designed the patient chairs from scratch. They were such a marvel of engineering that many manufacturers of hospital furnishings soon were emulating their design.

"It was a challenge to custom-design a comfortable, attractive chair that also met the stringent industry standards, but the chair we came up with was one of our proudest accomplishments," Rigenhagen said.

"And today, if you look in the catalogs of companies like Hill-Rom and Medline, you'll see a much more residential feel to their designs," he continued. "I think, in many respects, that's because of what was accomplished at Mid-Columbia Medical Center."

Rigenhagen said the MCMC job presented many other challenges besides those inherent to the task of making an institution feel more like an English country manor.

"The staff really was great through the whole process, but I know there were times when they hated seeing me coming," he said. "People don't like change, and what we were doing represented significant change. It was like everyone was trading up from a Volkswagen to a Porsche, which meant they all had to learn how to drive again."

Several years after the MCMC project was completed, Rigenhagen said, "I've never done any project that was as rewarding. It was just an amazing feeling to walk through the halls of that hospital and see an entire family gathered together in one of the activity rooms, just as we envisioned it happening."

In addition to the remarkable architectural changes, Scott made sure he kept a vow he had made to himself back in the dining hall at Pajaro Dunes. He jettisoned the long-used backless patient gowns that sacrificed patient dignity for caregiver convenience. Now, patients would wear plush robes that tied in the front, with several designs and colors from which to choose.

A new day truly had dawned at MCMC and, indeed, in healthcare. The significance wasn't lost on those who witnessed the hospital's startling transformation. To christen the new facility, MCMC planned a weekend of activities, including a community open house and a reception for employees, physicians and local dignitaries.

Ed Rosenbaum M.D., a Portland internist and author, was invited to speak at the reception. Rosenbaum could truly appreciate the Planetree philosophy of putting the patient's needs first. Years earlier, he had been a patient himself, undergoing cancer treatment. He had chronicled his frustrations with the medical system in a book titled *A Taste of My Own Medicine*, which in 1991 had been made into a movie called *The Doctor*, starring William Hurt.

Before the reception, Rosenbaum toured the new patient care units at MCMC. As he walked the halls and listened to Scott tell him about the new philosophy of care that would be unfolding at MCMC, the doctor quietly uttered the same three words over and over again. Later, when he stood up to address the room full of people attending the reception, Rosenbaum opened his comments with the same three words.

"It's about time," he said.

Thoughts *from* Leland Kaiser

WHY A HOSPITAL SHOULD BE
A SPIRITUAL ENVIRONMENT

Mark Scott viewed MCMC as a spiritual environment. As a result, he made spiritual features part of the design throughout the medical center campus.

In our new century, Mark's view will become the normative view of hospital administrators, who will increasingly view themselves as designers of healing spaces.

For the designer of healing spaces, the two major design dimensions of the universe are consciousness and space. We will define consciousness as basic awareness. What fills consciousness we refer to as space. Stimuli originating outside the body constitute outer space. Stimuli originating inside the body constitute inner space. Good patient care orchestrates the patient's experience in both inner and outer spaces.

Good patient design requires the use of scientific methodologies. One such methodology is phenomenology, which is defined as a study of the flow of inner consciousness.

In hospital design, we use architectural and environmental phenomenology to correlate patient consciousness with external stimuli, such as the shape of the room, colors in the room, presence of windows and music. Other branches of phenomenology look at the flow of inner stimuli created by dreams, visualizations, meditation or other mental and spiritual exercises.

In good patient care design, inner and outer stimuli are integrated for maximum therapeutic effect. Since consciousness has physical and nonphysical qualities, the patient care environment should be designed on both physical and nonphysical dimensions. Healing architecture lies along the physical dimension of patient space. Other design dimensions include interpersonal, emotional, mental, spiritual, social, existential and ontological variables.

Good design demands that all dimensions be integrated into one gestalt or overall design concept. If a hospital makes one statement in physical design and a conflicting statement in interpersonal relationships, confusion results for the patient and family.

The metaphor of drama is a good one to use in designing patient-care spaces. View the patient room as a stage. Conceptualize the rendering of patient care as a dramaturgical event. Perceive doctors and nurses as trained performers acting out their parts in a sacred play. Then, provide multiple opportunities for patients to experience their hospitalization as a life-transforming event.

Healing is a hands-on activity. It happens when we share our Being with our patients. It is largely independent of what we are doing for the patient. A massage therapist may maintain a healing presence for a patient while doing the massage. By contrast, a physician or nurse may be performing the right medical or nursing procedures without sharing Being or creating a healing presence for the patient.

Healing is high value-added and reaches beyond the realm of clinical objectivity and medical science. We are first and foremost human beings, children of the universe. That is who we are. We can add to that basic identity what we do: doctor, nurse, massage therapist or hospital administrator.

A total healing environment like MCMC was tuned to the multi-dimensionality of its patients. Staff was trained in Being as well as doing. Staff members needed to demonstrate competence on both dimensions.

Much of the healing activity that takes place in community hospitals occurs in the arena of complementary medicine, where alternative practitioners are working with traditional physicians to supplement the allopathic model. In the future, healing arts centers will become an integral part of the hospital or health campus, and their activities will be integrated with mainline medicine and nursing.

It is time for pioneering hospitals like MCMC to develop high-efficiency, patient-centered units where alternative therapies can be evaluated. These research and development units should constitute a safe harbor for innovation and discovery. The same evaluation criteria should be used for testing an alternative therapy, such as massage, as for evaluating any new drug or surgical procedure. Does it work? Under what conditions does it work? What are the contraindications? Is the whole thing worth the effort? MCMC started this ball rolling. Many other facilities will follow in its footsteps.

CHAPTER 4

CHANGING A CULTURE

The group of 20 casually dressed MCMC managers exited the rear of the hospital and strolled across the cobblestone commons area toward Mid-Columbia Medical Center's new, two-story office building. Near the entrance, the group passed a sandwich-board sign adorned with a "Now Appearing" header, under which was a list containing all of the managers' names and the MCMC departments they directed.

The managers entered the building, followed a long hallway and then filed into a dimly lit room. Three rows of chairs faced a small stage, at the rear of which was a large projector screen flanked by dark, plush curtains extending 20 feet in both directions. Each chair held a three-ring binder imprinted with a particular manager's name.

Moments after the managers took their seats, the room darkened completely, and the screen was illuminated with a bright blue wash, at the center of which was a white graphic — a tree encased in a circle under the words, "One Team; One School of Thought." As music reminiscent of a college fight song emanated from the speakers overhead, a spotlight bathed the stage in white light. Seconds later, Jim Hall, MCMC's director of human resources, entered stage-right from behind one of the curtains and greeted his colleagues.

"Welcome to the first-ever class of MCMC University," he said. "Thank you for being our guinea pigs."

As challenging as it was to reinvent the traditional notion of a hospital's physical environment, the far greater task, in Mark Scott's mind, would be changing the collective mindset of an entire healthcare organization.

After all, the physical transformation came with a set of plans. And although MCMC was entering new territory for a hospital, the project's architects, designers and contractors were not in completely uncharted waters — they were simply applying old principles to a new setting. But retraining each of the 600 human beings who worked, or the 200 who volunteered, at MCMC to ensure that they all thought as one in serving the hospital's customers? As Scott said, "There was no blueprint for that."

To create a training program, Scott would be working from scratch. He started the process by pulling together a group of managers for a two-day retreat and asking them: "How do we get our people on board? How do we immerse them in the Planetree philosophy to such an extent that we ensure every person who encounters anyone in this hospital clearly understands what we're trying to accomplish?"

MCMC's existing employee orientation program — the standard four-hour overview of dress codes, safety procedures, OSHA requirements and restroom locations — clearly wasn't the answer. Neither was putting people to sleep with didactic lectures about the importance of being nice to patients and guests.

"People had to leave this program with absolutely no doubt about how serious we were," Scott said. "They had to understand that this wasn't some flavor-of-the-month program that would just blow over. If we couldn't get every single person in our organization behind what we were doing, we were going to fail. Planetree wasn't just a program for the doctors and nurses and their patients. This was something that had to permeate our organization and positively impact every single person's encounter with us."

By the end of the retreat, Scott and the managers had a rough outline of a training program through which every existing employee — and all future new hires — would be sent, as well as volunteers, physicians[5] and their office staffs.

---

[5] An abbreviated version of the training program was developed for physicians to increase the likelihood they would break away from their busy practices and participate. Most did.

Called MCMC University, the intensive, 40-hour program would take each employee out of his or her regular work setting for eight hours daily over five days. Through guest speakers, videos, team-building exercises and role-playing opportunities, employees would learn what constituted exemplary customer service and how to provide it, the role of innovative thinking in the workplace and the importance of proper attitude.

They also would receive a comprehensive introduction to the principles of Planetree and learn their role in ensuring that MCMC's deep commitment to the bold new venture was apparent to every patient, family member, vendor or any other visitor.

Because they were charting new territory in healthcare training, Scott and the management team borrowed liberally from the best practices of major corporations renowned for their customer service. The first MCMC University curriculum would have struck familiar chords with employees of Disney, Ritz-Carlton, Semantec or Mary Kay Cosmetics, in particular.

"That original curriculum was fairly rough, but we were making it up on the fly," Scott said. "We knew we weren't going to find what we needed by looking around the hospital industry, where everybody was doing the same kind of training we had been. So we decided we'd borrow ideas from the best in the customer service business — companies that were doing really innovative, transformational service work."

The MCMC University program was built around a variation of Disney's *on-stage, off-stage* employee performance philosophy. MCMC staff would learn they were expected to assume the role of performers at work (on-stage) and be responsible for creating memorable experiences for customers. That meant personal problems would have to be checked at the door (off-stage).

To reinforce the motif, a theater setting was created in the training area. Employees would spend much of their class time actually on stage, role-playing, creating and acting out skits that demonstrated quality service or presenting the results of team-building exercises. The MCMC University slogan ("One Team; One School of Thought") and the specially created "fight song" that trainees heard when they first arrived served as reminders that this was a setting for higher learning and innovation.

"It was important that this be a special environment, that we transported people out of their normal, daily settings and let them know they were truly entering higher ground in healthcare," Scott said.

To help create the MCMC University milieu, Scott hired consultant Marc Bowen, who specialized in corporate training productions. "I had done some theater productions and employee-training programs for some large corporations, but I had never seen anything like what MCMC was doing," Bowen said. "It was an amazing commitment."

"Students" would spend a considerable amount of their time touring every hospital department and affiliate, which Scott felt was one of the most critical components of the university experience. He knew that, like most large organizations, MCMC was more a collection of related clans than a single, cohesive family. MCMC was no mega-corporation. Still, there were people throughout the hospital who were serving the same patients, but who had never met and who had little understanding of the importance of each other's roles in accomplishing the organization's goals.

"I wanted people to get an idea about what everybody did at MCMC," Scott said. "When you're working hard at the same job day-after-day, it's easy to get myopic and forget how important every person is to the overall success of an organization, or, in this case, what amounted to a new way of doing business."

In advance of the maiden tour of managers who comprised MCMC University's first class, each hospital department was instructed to create its own experience for the touring students. Employees were encouraged to be as creative as possible while providing an overview of their department's operations and various functions.

That first series of tours, while departments were still auditioning their material, was fairly ordinary, Scott felt. Except for one department: the MCMC laboratory. There, a phlebotomist named Randy Carter directed a comprehensive and entertaining tour, which included a hands-on exercise and a lively discussion of how the department's employees intended to personalize, humanize and demystify the lab experience for patients.

Articulate and personable, Carter had a natural flair for both education and entertainment, Scott observed. It wasn't Scott's first encounter with the young lab employee, but it was the first time he had seen Carter in this light. The two had met when Carter worked in the local cycle shop where Scott took his bike for repairs. When Carter left the shop for MCMC, he intended for it to be a short stop on his way to medical school. But Scott threw a detour in front of him.

"We were planning to hire someone after the first university session to facilitate the rest of the training," Scott said. "After I saw Randy's presentation, I knew he would be perfect for the job."

Scott had always looked within his organization first when filling management vacancies. Several of his department directors were individuals who possessed a lot more in the way of street smarts and personality than relevant experience. Scott had watched several management stars emerge after he entrusted them with more responsibility. Carter, who had been at MCMC only six months, would be his next star in training.

The initial MCMC University session (rehearsal may be a better word) with the department directors kicked off an ambitious effort to train all 600 of MCMC's employees. It was a process that would run for 26 consecutive weeks. The training would consume close to half-a-million dollars in lost work time and would require department directors to become adept at juggling schedules to compensate for the loss of their employees during class time. But because Scott knew it only took one person to turn a great hospital experience into a mundane or poor one, he insisted that everyone within his organization attend the university. That included MCMC's entire contingent of volunteers.

"We were saying to our people in no uncertain terms, 'You are important to our organization; you have something to offer; and we want to prepare you for success,'" Scott said. "That was an important statement to make to ensure everyone was on board with us and knew they had a role to play. We had to show the housekeepers, maintenance staff, the business office personnel, everyone, what it meant to personalize, humanize and demystify what they did."

MCMC University also provided an opportunity for each person in the organization to determine if this new approach to doing business was going to be a good fit for him or her.

"It gave us the chance to gather everyone together — the disenchanted, disgruntled and disheartened, along with the absolutely enthused — and say: 'Wherever you are now, we are all moving forward together,'" said Carter, who assumed direction of the training program after the first dry-run session with managers. "We could tell each employee very honestly that he or she was there for the next 40 hours to help us create our future."

Each university class was composed of a diverse cross-section of MCMC employees. Carter purposely filled each session with employees from different departments. These were individuals whose patient responsibilities regularly overlapped, but who rarely crossed each other's paths.

"That turned out to be an extremely effective strategy," Carter remembered. "We would put into the same class, for example, someone from the intensive care unit and someone from the ER [emergency room] and someone from the laboratory and someone from patient registration. Those are departments that would work together frequently, but maybe not really understand what the other departments did, except in general terms.

"When we put them together for their week of training, we were hopeful that we'd see relationships developing that would have a lasting impact in the working environment. People would gain an understanding and appreciation for what other members of their extended team did. The benefits of that approach are still being felt in the organization today."

MCMC University students experienced a production that had been staged as meticulously as a Broadway play, starting with the personalized invitation they received in their home mailboxes. Each morning or afternoon, they passed their names in bold type on the marquee set up in the common area between the main hospital and the medical office building. The intended effect was to extend a personal welcome to current students and to help build awareness and a sense of anticipation among employees whose university experience was yet to come.

Other details also helped make the university experience a special one. For example, each student received the class syllabus and an array of educational materials packaged in a personalized three-ring binder. Chairs and tables were rearranged regularly to break up the monotony of long tables facing the front of the room.

The curriculum was developed specifically to reduce the risk of wandering attentions, which meant the emphasis was on involving and engaging participants as much as possible. Fully half of the program was devoted to the department tours, which served the dual purpose of exposing students to the rest of the organization and keeping the blood flowing in their legs and brains.

The tours went through every MCMC department, and Carter spent a lot of time working to ensure the philosophy of the university setting extended to the field trips. "We actually went to each department and helped them script their tour to ensure they were engaging and informative and fun," he said.

Carter had caught Scott's eye by developing a lab tour that had university students dressing in lab coats and actually performing procedures. Soon, with Carter's guidance, the other hospital departments were staging experiences that were equally entertaining and educational.

Back in the classroom, upper management personnel were featured prominently in training sessions. Scott opened each session with an overview of Planetree and what it would mean for patients, the departments and each individual. He was scheduled for an hour and 15 minutes, but his enthusiasm for the program and desire to answer every question invariably took him over his scheduled time. In the tightly timed environment of the university setting, speakers who ran long may have elevated Carter's blood pressure. But it wasn't every day that MCMC employees got to have a conversation with their leader so, in Scott's case, Carter made an exception.

"Our program had to be amazing," Carter said. "When you came to MCMC University, you had to have a remarkable experience. It wasn't okay to have a good experience or even a very good experience. This had to be something that absolutely shook you — from the staging to the performance of the speakers to the faculty remembering each student's name. We were teaching people that when serving our customers, 'B's' were not okay; we were going to higher ground in healthcare. Our attention to detail had to be remarkable and apparent in every aspect of that program."

Day-in and day-out, for six months, while the interior walls of the hospital were being torn down and rebuilt on the other side of the common area, Scott, Carter and the training staff continued the process of reconstructing the collective mindset of their organization.

Early on, it was difficult for Scott to tell what, if anything, was happening to the culture of his organization as growing numbers of employees were receiving their Planetree training. Employees were earning their MCMC University diplomas and heading back to their jobs, but were they putting any of their lessons into action? The remodeling project was still under way; Planetree had yet to be officially switched on. Still, Scott hoped he'd be getting a running start, that his new grads would be practicing their lessons, wowing patients and guests and beginning to infect the rest of the organization with their new service orientation.

Certainly Scott was encouraged by his employees' almost universally positive reaction to their university experience and their acceptance of the changes they were being asked to make. He'd frequently walk by the classroom at the end of a session and see groups of employees lingering and speaking enthusiastically about that morning's or afternoon's program. And Scott was hearing nothing from the ranks that would indicate employees were not buying into the Planetree concept; with only a few exceptions, employees and managers alike seemed to be "getting it."

In fact, Carter said, "I can only identify three employees who just couldn't buy into this and left the organization because of it."

One of those who did leave had been one of Scott's best and most trusted managers for many years. He was a key leader in the organization, with dozens of employees under his watch, but he wasn't buying into the new way of doing business.

The decision to let the popular manager go was extremely difficult for Scott, but it served as a wake-up call to all MCMC employees that, all these months later, the train for Chicago hadn't veered off track.

There would be other individuals who were slow to come around. "We had some nurses who still weren't totally convinced," Scott said. "They'd tell me 'I'm just not into this patient empowerment thing.' And I'd tell them, 'That's your prerogative, but that's what we are going to be doing here. There are all kinds of hospitals where you can go do the kind of nursing you're used to.'"

As the weeks passed, and more and more of the MCMC family had gone through the university, Scott and Carter began to sense that the tide had shifted. As Carter described it, "There was a time when we felt like we hit critical mass — a time when all the new words and concepts were seeping into regular conversations and into people's actions in a very natural way."

MCMC's cultural transformation was under way.

Thoughts *from* Leland Kaiser

HOW STRONG LEADERS CAN USE "OPPORTUNITY SPACE" TO OVERCOME RESISTANCE

That Mark Scott didn't meet with more resistance in his organization is probably a result of his determination, powers of persuasion, leadership skills and the strength of the Planetree program. And, of course, the quality of his board, staff and physicians, and their faith in his conviction.

Few leaders attempting to affect such profound organizational change could expect to be so fortunate.

As soon as you let someone know you are about to change his or her life, you will be met with resistance. Everyone who is not prepared to take the trip with you will meet you with resistance, as was the case for Mark Scott in the early going with his nurses.

But resistance is good. It is the counter-reaction you are looking for. In fact, it's likely you haven't achieved what you set out to unless you receive some resistance.

There is a term called "holding the space," which is when someone creates an environment where what is inside others can come out. To hold the space is to offer permission, support, rewards and encouragement to allow the person to realize and draw out the potential from within.

The board of directors of MCMC held the space for Mark Scott, arming him with the courage and confidence to rally his people behind his cause — to hold the opportunity space for them.

I don't know of any adventurous chief executive officer who doesn't have a board that permits new ideas. But how do you win over a board and convince them to let you do a job they didn't hire you to do?

There is another term called "idiosyncratic credit" that says, "You can be as idiosyncratic as you want, and we will accept that, as long as you are good enough." In other words, the amount of craziness people will tolerate in you is directly proportionate to how good you are at what you are doing for them.

Many years ago, psychologist Kenneth Gergen wrote about behavior exchange, which, simply put, says "What I give you, and what you give me, we both value." As long as that exchange is in place, we allow each other tremendous elbow room.

What leaders need to find out is what enables their boards to give them the room to be creative. What are the payoffs for your board? The more you develop momentum, the harder it is to stop you.

Typically, the opportunity space is much larger than most leaders think it is. They don't realize how much wiggle room they truly have and that they could be doing a lot more than they are doing.

Overcoming resistance from employees and others is often a matter of overcoming fear. Fear is what holds people back. Fear always causes containment. When people feel fearful, they try to secure their space. To overcome fear, you have to do the opposite. You have to push out. It's expansion, not containment. Those who are successful are expansive. A feeling of euphoria — the excitement, the fun — overcomes their fear.

Negative predictions are based on fear. Positive predictions are based on euphoria. Trust is as important as euphoria. Something has to offset the fear. Trust enables us to understand that it's going to be okay. Trust and euphoria move you beyond fear.

Each of us needs to be in a state of readiness. I often send people to MCMC to increase their state of readiness. When you walk it and talk it, you realize it could happen. You are more ready for it.

Most of Mark Scott's resistance came from his nursing staff. But when he began sending them to see Planetree, their resistance all but evaporated. They saw it could work. They were ready for it.

Every organization will have "plug-pullers," people who will do everything they can to derail change. It's critical to get them on board or, if necessary, leave them behind.

CHAPTER 5

OPENING
THE BOOKS

Scott knew that a critical component of the Planetree concept was to give patients complete access to both their own medical records and to a full library of easy-to-understand information about their medical condition. By demystifying their illness, Planetree allows patients to be part of their own cure.

Already, Scott had essentially won support from his physicians for opening up patients' medical records. He knew that some of his doctors also were already sold on the public library component of Planetree. But he suspected that others would be alarmed by the notion of arming patients with comprehensive information about their medical conditions and treatment options.

Scott was content to let the library idea simmer on the back burner for a while so he could focus on more pressing matters. He was still immersed in the massive hospital remodeling project, the implementation of a new nursing model, the retraining of an entire workforce and his ongoing sales pitch with his medical staff.

He had visited the modest patient library across the street from California Pacific Medical Center in San Francisco and figured he would create something similar for Mid-Columbia Medical Center — just not yet.

"I knew how important the information piece was to (Planetree founder) Angie Thieriot," Scott said. "And throughout our construction, and during the nursing retreats and employee training, Robin Orr was constantly reminding me about the library. But I had about as much as

I could handle at the time."

Scott's priorities changed abruptly, however, when his longtime board member and friend, Charles Harding, was diagnosed with cancer. When Scott had been casting around in his mind for a possible champion who could help him move the library project forward, Harding was not the first person who came to mind.

Smart, loyal and universally beloved as Harding was, the grandfatherly meat-locker owner did not seem a likely candidate to be the catalyst who would break down barriers and clear the way to open the doors of a beautiful new health library.

Harding, in his mid-60s, may have held the lofty title of MCMC's chairman of the board, but he was just Chuck to the many who knew and revered him. Modest and genteel, he was the longtime owner and operator of Harding's Meat Market at the east end of The Dalles. Outwardly, Harding was the ultimate "good old boy," but that didn't belie the fact that he was a savvy businessman who had become a trusted confidant, respected adviser and ardent supporter of Scott and MCMC.

Not long after Scott learned of Harding's cancer diagnosis, his friend approached him with a request. "Chuck remembered hearing about the Planetree library in San Francisco, and he wondered if it was possible for him to get some information about the particular kind of cancer he had," Scott remembered.

Scott forwarded the request to the director of California Pacific's Planetree library, Tracy Cosgrove, who compiled and sent Harding a detailed packet of information about his disease. Harding pored over the information and then set up an appointment with his internist in The Dalles to discuss the material and ask a few questions.

"Chuck takes all this information to his appointment because he has this lethal disease," said Scott. "He wants to learn all he can about it, so he can fight back. His doctor tells him, 'I don't have time for that.' Appointment over. This physician, like other physicians, wasn't sure what to do with a patient who was empowered with information. The model was, 'I'm the doctor; I know what's best. I call the shots; you do as you're told.' The initial response to being confronted with a somewhat knowledgeable patient was to feel intimidated."

Fortunately, this physician's reticence was short-lived. On his way home from the office that same evening, the doctor stopped at Harding's residence and went through the packet of information with his patient. When Scott heard the story, he knew he now had a champion for the health information library. He also knew that the project needed a higher spot on his priority list.

To this point, the development of Planetree at MCMC had as often as not been the result of key players being in the right place at the right time. Scott hearing Robin Orr at Pajaro Dunes. Randy Carter wowing Scott during an MCMC laboratory tour. And now, another key player was about to appear at just the right time. In May 1991, Michele Spatz found herself reading job postings at an annual meeting of medical librarians in San Francisco, the birthplace of Planetree.

As Spatz read, she came across a job posting that described a job she thought existed only in her dreams. When she finished reading the description, she had two questions: What's a Planetree, and where in the world is The Dalles, Oregon?

As director of the Library of the Health Sciences of the University of Illinois College of Medicine at Peoria, Spatz knew there was a huge gap between what patients and consumers wanted in health information and what was available to them. Day-after-day, she would watch patients wander into her library after their clinic visits, navigate their way through the metal detectors and enter an information fortress, literally and figuratively. The long rows and towering stacks of medical tomes were physically intimidating and all but impenetrable to anyone without a medical degree.

"Over-and-over, I would watch these people come in off the street looking for any kind of information that would help them better understand their medical condition," Spatz remembered. "We had absolutely nothing to offer them."

The public library system was no better resource, and the Internet and its universe of information was years away from being accessible to the public.

In time, Spatz would spearhead a community-based effort in Peoria to begin to address the growing demand for consumer-friendly health information. She helped create a coalition composed of representatives of the community's libraries, which included the public library system and three teaching hospitals. The group developed a core list of basic resource materials that each library would add to its collection to assist consumers looking for general health information.

The list and materials were shared with the 70 libraries in the rural communities surrounding Peoria, and training sessions were held to teach public librarians how to use the resources. A networking system was developed to ensure that, if one librarian couldn't answer a consumer's health question, he or she had access to another who could. Spatz also began writing a monthly column that was sent to librarians listing additional resources for consumer health information.

In her efforts to give patients and consumers better access to understandable health information, Spatz unwittingly was building a resume that was tailor-made for the new position Mark Scott had just created: MCMC's consumer health librarian. When Spatz read Scott's job description, it sounded to her like an ideal opportunity to make an exciting career move — even though that move might be halfway to the middle of nowhere.

"I had no idea where The Dalles was, but it sounded very picturesque from the description," she said. "I was really hooked by the description of the job and the opportunity to take my interest and passion directly to the public. I saw this library as a chance to be the first stop in someone's quest for information, rather than the last resort."

As new as the Planetree concept was, Scott never expected to find a candidate to direct his new library who actually had experience in a consumer health information setting. Finding Spatz was just one more sign to Scott that his bold Planetree experience was meant to be.

By the time Spatz arrived for her interview at MCMC, the Planetree library had joined the four or five other massive initiatives that were now at the top of Scott's priorities. True to form, when Scott dove into the library project, he did so determined to ensure his facility would be the showcase of the Planetree organization.

While impressed with California Pacific's modest consumer library, Scott had not been inspired enough by it to take MCMC's library off the back burner. But after Harding's cancer diagnosis reordered his priorities, Scott and staff members made another trip to the Bay Area, this time to visit the consumer health library at San Jose Medical Center (SJMC), the site of another Planetree pilot unit. SJMC had set up its library away from the hospital in a small, remodeled Victorian house. The facility was warm and inviting, the furniture comfortable, and Scott felt its location away from the hospital made it much less intimidating and more accessible to the public.

"I saw the San Jose library and thought, 'This is what the library should feel like,'" Scott said. "It shouldn't be in a hospital lobby. This is a personal thing, and people should be able to do research on their medical condition in a less-threatening environment."

Not long after Scott returned from San Jose, MCMC purchased a stately, but badly run-down Victorian home on a well-traveled street in downtown The Dalles. More than 150 years old, the home was on the verge of being torn down to make room for a parking lot when Scott gave it a new lease on life.

The Planetree Health Resource Center opened in the beautifully refurbished Victorian on June 2, 1992. A tasteful wood sign hanging from the porch roof announced the name Scott chose for the new community showcase: The Harding House. Chuck had lost his battle with cancer a few months earlier, but Scott would make sure the new public health library would serve as a legacy to his friend's determination and commitment to improving healthcare in his beloved hometown.

The entire first floor of the new library was devoted to a vast array of health resource materials, which Spatz had compiled with the assistance of the staff at Planetree's San Francisco home base. Oak bookshelves lining the walls held row-upon-row of medical books, from easy-to-understand preventive health titles to disease-specific reference guides. Spatz subscribed to a wide range of periodicals, from consumer-oriented magazines such as *Arthritis Today* to the *New England Journal of Medicine* and the *Journal of the American Medical Association.*

A wall of file cabinets housed Planetree's precursor to the Internet — a vast and continually updated collection of clippings of health and medical articles from newspapers and magazines around the world.

In a separate room at the back of the comfortable new library, four computer stations gave visitors access to electronic medical databases and interactive CD-ROM programs.

Fact sheets, written by Spatz and her assistant, Linda Stahl, provided visitors with easy-to-digest information on medical conditions and other topics.

One large, open room served as a classroom that could host 40 people for regularly scheduled community education programs presented by hospital and community-based health professionals and others.

Artwork and comfortable seating encouraged visitors to linger in the library for as long as they liked, exploring on their own or being guided by Spatz or Stahl.

In addition to serving the community in general, Spatz and Stahl also were, in the Planetree model, integral members of MCMC's patient care team. Their role was to compile comprehensive information packets for MCMC patients who were interested in receiving them, either customized to their specific medical condition or on other health-related topics they or a family member desired.

"Planetree was all about choices, so we weren't going to force our patients to participate in any aspect of the program," Scott said. "But we knew those patient information packets would be popular because they would be personalized to whatever condition put that person in the hospital."

Added Spatz: "No two patients with diabetes would ever get identical information in their packets. Each packet focused on the specific issues each patient thought were important. They would include not only information about the patient's condition, but also topics like treatment options, risks versus benefits of the options and lifestyle adjustments they could make to minimize the impact their condition had on their overall health and well-being."

Scott knew the information packets would represent another thorn in the side of those members of the medical staff he hadn't yet converted to the Planetree gospel. It wouldn't help that the packets addressed *whatever* information the patient requested, and they were not medically abridged.

"If patients wanted detailed research done on their illness, we were going to give them everything we had," Scott said. "If they wanted information on alternative therapies, that meant we were going to give it to them. At the time, that was fairly radical thinking, and we knew we were going to be stepping on some toes. But the patient had a right to have this information.

"As physicians became aware that patients were getting this information, a few came unglued because they thought we were giving patients 'wacko' articles," Scott continued. "In each case, I'd tell them, 'Look, your patient requested this information; it's your job to go through it with him, and if you don't believe it, explain why. Ultimately, the patient still gets to decide what course he wants to follow, but with your help he'll be making an informed decision.'"

Having spent her entire career working with physicians, Spatz knew Planetree's information component would not immediately be embraced by the entire MCMC medical staff. "Medicine had always been shrouded in secrecy, and a lot of doctors preferred it that way," she said.

Still, the day the doors opened to the Planetree Health Resource Center, in the beautifully restored Harding House, Spatz knew she had made the right career move.

"From the day the center opened, I knew it was going to be successful, no matter how much resistance there was from the medical or nursing staff," she said. "Once the public started coming in, I knew that the consumers would carry our mission forward. I remember one doctor confronting me and saying, 'I will never send a patient of mine to your library.' Several months later, I was talking to a visitor, and I asked her how she found us. She said her doctor sent her. It turned out her physician was Dr. I'll Never Send a Patient of Mine to You."

Thoughts *from* Leland Kaiser

EMPOWERING PATIENTS TO BE HEALTHCARE PARTNERS

At MCMC, patients are viewed as healthcare partners. They partner with their clinical caregivers. Rather than being passive recipients of care, they are afforded an opportunity to become active participants in the clinical decision-making process. They are encouraged to visit the hospital medical library to learn about their medical condition. In addition, they have access to their medical record and can make notes on their progress and experiences in the facility. This is the real meaning of patient-centered care, but it is seldom realized in contemporary treatment settings. Usually, care is organized around the convenience of the staff, not the needs of the patient.

Patient care at MCMC represents a revolutionary change when compared with what happens in most community hospitals in America, where members of the clinical staff are viewed as experts; patients are seen as uninformed, passive recipients of care; and family members are regarded, at best, as necessary nuisances.

Mark's passionate patient advocacy was largely responsible for the existence of these revolutionary attitudes. A caring culture does not happen by accident in any institution. It is a daily work of love. It requires both a values champion and a supportive staff. Of course, patients, family members and the community at large are the most important beneficiaries of this kind of patient-centric culture. It is sometimes described in the literature. It seldom exists in reality.

Usually, patients lose most of their personal freedoms and capacity for self-determination when they are hospitalized. As a result, they regress. At MCMC, they are given many freedoms and numerous choice points. They are expected to exert a measure of control over what happens to them. As a result, they progress, rather than regress, in this type of patient-care setting.

Patients are either empowered or disempowered by those who care for them. Caregivers trained in the health professions at traditional schools are not usually taught to view their patients as partners, but rather as passive recipients. Often a caregiver will not even discuss a patient's diagnosis with the patient when asked a question. This leads to a complete communication breakdown, as well as suspicion and alienation on the patient's part. Essentially, this attitude shows disrespect for the patient.

Mark worked hard to educate this regressive attitude out of all clinical-care givers at MCMC. By and large, he succeeded, with only a few chronic holdouts who could not bear to see the patient as both a peer and a patient.

A mundane organization may accomplish the expected. It will never realize the unexpected. The real question is: What is your role in the unfolding drama of healthcare? Are you conscious of the role you play, or are you a blind agent of the status quo?

The universe is a system within a system within a system. The microcosm reflects the macrocosm. As the ancient adage says, "As above, so below." This means the universe is reflective. Each layer reflects the layer above and below. Nothing stands alone. Everything is connected. Change one thing, and you change everything.

Every change on earth is reflected in heaven. Every change in heaven is reflected on earth. The universe is a giant hologram. The All is in every part, and every part is in the All. This gives tremendous power to the actions of the part.

To apply this idea, your hospital has the power to change the American healthcare industry by becoming a destination hospital where new possibilities are invented and made available to the industry. The highest level of management is creation. This is, indeed, high drama! This is precisely what happened at MCMC.

CHAPTER 6

NURSING THE NURSES

Neither Roberta Carson nor Tia Bailey, both natives of Southern states, ever imagined they'd find their nursing nirvana in a remote part of the Northwest. Over the course of their long nursing careers, both of them had become increasingly disillusioned with the profession.

Since she was seven years old, Carson had never considered being anything other than a nurse. As a child, she had spent many hours in the waiting room of a Veterans Administration hospital while her father, a World War II vet, struggled through a long list of illnesses. The experience left her feeling powerless, yet determined to one day be able to help others like her father.

But the nursing career she had envisioned all those years was not the nursing career she was experiencing. Her epiphany didn't come out of the clear blue sky; it was hand-delivered in 1980 by an irate physician. Standing in the hallway of a hospital in Arkansas, absorbing the tongue-lashing of the doctor who could not believe she'd shared a temperature reading with the patient, Carson realized that her lifelong desire to truly care for people was just a dream.

Bailey, by contrast, hadn't thought of being a nurse until her father presented her with a career proposal upon her graduation from high school. "I'll pay for your training," he told her, "as long as you become a teacher, secretary or nurse."

Bailey's grandmother had been a nurse, as had a great-aunt. Her hometown of Amarillo, Texas, had three good nursing schools. One of Bailey's sisters already had chosen teaching; the other became a secretary.

Nursing was the logical choice, and once into her education, Bailey quickly developed a passion for it.

After nursing school, Bailey entered the profession determined to tackle the most technically challenging nursing venues she could find, like intensive care, acute care and dialysis. She was advancing her skills and her career rapidly, but along the way, she was becoming disenchanted with her profession.

She began to feel that patients were not treated well in the healthcare system, and that too often she was expected to do things *to* patients, rather than *for* them. She found it dehumanizing and demoralizing for herself and her patients and their families.

"The healthcare setting of the '70s and '80s was deadly for maintaining a healthy emotional connection to your practice," Bailey said. "The goal seemed to be how *long* can we keep someone alive, rather than how *well* we can keep them alive."

For both Carson and Bailey, it was time for a change.

Carson's husband, Carl, discovered Mid-Columbia Medical Center and The Dalles when he inquired about a radiologic technologist job he'd seen advertised. The ad described a small, rural hospital that was attempting to reshape itself from the patient's perspective. The Carsons thought the concept was intriguing enough to at least warrant a phone call. At the same time, they knew only a remarkable opportunity would convince them to leave their longtime home in El Dorado, Arkansas, and relocate across the country. They knew they'd found that opportunity as soon as they arrived at MCMC for Carl's interview in 1989.

"We fell in love with the place immediately," said Roberta Carson, who joined the staff with her husband.

Bailey's arrival at MCMC came 10 years after Carson's. Bailey and her husband had become intrigued with the Pacific Northwest after they visited her sister, who lived in Goldendale, Washington, about 30 miles north of The Dalles. After that visit, the Baileys agreed they'd be back for good someday. It wouldn't take long.

Bailey researched the healthcare facilities in the area, discovered MCMC, made a call and was hired over the phone. She had never laid eyes on The Dalles or the hospital, which was in the early stages of a monumental makeover that included a dramatic shift in the traditional role of the nurse. Or, rather, a return to the kind of nursing that Carson and Bailey (and, undoubtedly, so many other nurses) had imagined but never actually practiced.

"I had no idea what I was getting into," Bailey said. "But I was ready for a change, and the new nursing model that Mid-Columbia Medical Center was describing sounded too good to be true."

Prior to the early 1980s, MCMC used a team model of nursing care. In team nursing, several layers of providers were involved in the care of each patient. The MCMC nursing staff, at that time, was predominantly composed of licensed practical nurses (L.P.N.s) and certified nursing aides. With better-trained registered nurses (R.N.s) representing only about 15 percent of the staff, the team approach offered the most effective way to take advantage of MCMC's limited professional nursing expertise.

"Nursing at MCMC at that time was essentially the same as at many other hospitals," recalled Joyce Powell-Morin, R.N., a native of The Dalles who had been with MCMC her entire career. "The largest volume of our caregivers were nonprofessionals, and they were the ones with most of the patient contact. With so few registered nurses, we were just in and out of the patient rooms, either checking in very briefly or making rounds with the doctor."

Over time, MCMC replaced nonprofessionals with registered nurses, which allowed for a shift in the early 1980s from the team model to modular nursing. Modular nursing took better advantage of the increasing numbers of R.N.s and also got the trained caregivers closer to their patients.

Each floor's large, centralized station, through which all nursing activity passed, was replaced with smaller modules spaced throughout the patient wings. With more registered nurses on hand, they could be teamed with an aide or L.P.N. and assigned fewer patients, increasing patient contact, attention and quality of care.

The modular nursing concept had its flaws. For example, more nursing stations increased the odds that conversations between caregivers about patients could be overheard. The modular furniture used to create each unit was inefficient and uncomfortable for the nurses and also kept the traditional barriers between nurse and patient in place. But even though it wasn't perfect, the modular approach was a step in the right direction that would leave MCMC nurses better positioned to transition to the new Planetree approach.

Of course, in the 1980s, no one at MCMC — or any other hospital for that matter — was thinking much about how a nursing model might affect patients. Issues like confidentiality weren't of the greatest importance in a hospital that still wrote the names of each patient on white boards hanging in the hallways. And the concept of building walls between caregiver and patient? The higher the better.

Only with the benefit of hindsight, and the shift in focus from caregiver to patient that Planetree proposed, would those notions suddenly seem archaic.

Mark Scott knew that, more than anyone or anything else, nurses were critical to the success of the Planetree program. Scott had to have them on board 100 percent. By the time Planetree went live at MCMC in spring 1992, he was confident that they were — although getting there had been a long, hard road.

During his initial Planetree sales campaign, Scott had been flabbergasted that any nurse would not immediately embrace a new model that gave her or him a significantly greater role in each patient's care, and the chance to teach and to truly practice healing nursing. Many nurses, like Carson and Bailey, were encouraged by the concept, but past disappointments had left them skeptical.

"I think my spirit was broken by the time I came to MCMC," Carson said. "Nursing afforded me a way to make a good living, but I had given up the thought that I could ever be personally nurtured by a nursing career. A lot of us felt the same way. We'd spend our days running around, just putting out fires. At the end of the day, you'd be exhausted — and feeling like you hadn't done a single thing for your patients. So, when Mark started talking about Planetree, many of us were wondering if this was just some crazy idea of the day. We just couldn't see it ever really happening."

Gradually, though, that skepticism began to give way to guarded optimism and, ultimately, enthusiasm. Traveling to San Francisco and seeing Planetree in action was a good start for many on the nursing staff; others converted to Scott's gospel during retreats. Each time nurses were asked for an opinion or input during the development of the nursing component or the design of the new units, they came closer to believing Scott might be serious.

As Scott saw it, any nurse who hadn't been converted by the time he was ready to go live with Planetree would probably be happier working at another hospital and practicing nursing as usual.

"We knew we wouldn't reach every nurse, and that was okay," he said. "Not everyone was ready for the change, and we lost some people. But those who stayed felt good about the process and were excited to get Planetree implemented."

Bailey agreed, saying, "The decision to become a Planetree hospital may have been made without my input, but being included after the decision made me feel valued."

Planetree's notion of patient care was a 180-degree swing from the traditional model in which physicians delivered orders to nurses, who executed the care with patients who, for the most part, were passive observers in the process. Planetree reversed the hierarchy. Patients were given the opportunity to help direct their own care and were encouraged, though never compelled, to actively participate in the decision-making process.

Physicians and nurses would be required to relinquish some of the control to which they were accustomed and to practice a more team-oriented approach. Now the captain would be the patient, not the care professional.

The Planetree nurse and physician would have to be skilled professionals and also teachers and information therapists, arming patients with enough knowledge to participate in the development of their own care plan.

The concept of patient choice was truly foreign in America's hospitals. It would require major adjustments by MCMC's medical and nursing staffs, not to mention patients who were used to having care simply delivered to them.

But after spending their careers taking orders from physicians and not having much input themselves, MCMC's nurses relished the opportunity to put their skills and knowledge to better use in a true patient-care partnership. To help facilitate the process, MCMC moved into a shared governance model of nursing, delegating the bulk of the day-to-day decision-making to the people who lived with the consequences of the decisions.

"By shifting to the shared governance model, we were saying to our nurses, 'Within these guidelines, you figure out what needs to be done in order for you to deliver your patients the best care,'" said longtime MCMC nurse Powell-Morin.

While empowering to nurses, the Planetree model also required a different mindset. "Although by now our nurses were generally on board with Planetree, and for the most part eager to implement it, the program represented a dramatic change," said Scott. "And that was scary for many."

Powell-Morin said the nurses' fear was about letting go of control. "Nurses had always been compassionate, but also somewhat matriarchal or patriarchal," she said.

Relinquishing control, offering patients choices, giving them information and facilitating their more active participation would not come naturally or, in many instances, easily to nurses educated and experienced in the "old ways" of their profession. That said, Planetree offered the MCMC nurses their first opportunity to practice the kind of nursing most had envisioned but had never been able to put into action.

To help facilitate patient participation, Planetree created a new nursing position, the care-partner coordinator. This new discipline was charged with orienting each patient and his or her family and friends to MCMC's new way of providing care. The model also encouraged each patient's family and friends to become actively involved in their loved one's care.

The timing of Planetree's implementation at MCMC coincided with the American hospital industry's growing push to reduce the length of patient stays. Faced with declining reimbursements from Medicare and private insurers, hospitals were struggling to develop and implement more efficient ways to deliver their services and discharge patients faster.

In an environment that had witnessed the closure of some of the nation's hospitals, MCMC's commitment to the Planetree transformation may have seemed a questionable use of precious financial resources. But, beyond Scott's more humanistic motives for implementing Planetree, he also believed it was a smart business move.

First, with healthcare becoming increasingly competitive, and with a rival hospital less than 20 miles away in Hood River, Scott felt Planetree's patient-centered approach would give MCMC a significant competitive edge. More than that, giving patients and family members the opportunity to be intimately involved in their own care process and better educated about their illness or surgery would better prepare them to continue their care at home or in another care setting. Shorter hospital stays went right to MCMC's bottom line.

"From the beginning, Planetree made good business sense to me," Scott said. "If, from the moment a patient enters your hospital, you begin a highly personalized education process, you are going to be much better positioned to get him or her out of your hospital bed."

MCMC patients knew it was no longer business as usual at their community hospital virtually the moment they were admitted. The physical changes were striking enough on the trip from the admitting desk through the main hallways, into the elevator and into their pleasantly decorated rooms. But soon after they had reached their room, they would meet their care-partner coordinator who would introduce them to a hospital environment they had never imagined.

They would be told about MCMC's staff massage therapists, who were available upon request to ease their stress or help prepare them for surgery or a procedure. They would learn about the art cart that would be wheeled by a volunteer into their room, allowing them to adorn the walls during their stay with paintings or posters of their choosing. They would hear about the full-time staff person whose primary responsibility was to tell therapeutic stories to patients and families.

Family members, friends and able patients were given tours of the nursing unit. As they passed the open nursing station, patients were shown the oak shelf where later they could find their medical record. They were told it was theirs, and they were free to read it at any time, make their own notes, and ask their nurse or doctor questions about any of its contents

Stopping at the kitchen/dining area, they would be invited to bring their own food to cook and enjoy together, which would enable them to stay with their loved ones as long as they wanted. MCMC no longer had visiting hours; visitors could come and go as they pleased.

To alleviate the fear and sense of isolation generated by confinement in a hospital, spouses, parents, children and friends were invited to visit the unit at any hour and even to stay overnight if they wished. They were welcome to sleep on the chairs that converted into beds in the patient rooms or to rest in one of the quiet rooms located on each unit and set aside for family and friends.

The care-partner coordinator would inform each patient about MCMC's comprehensive consumer health-information program. Patients and family members would be invited to visit the comfortable patient library in the middle of the unit. They were urged to request an information packet from the Planetree Health Resource Center to help them better understand their condition.

Patients were even told that if they had questions about, or an interest in, a nontraditional therapy, such as chiropractic or healing touch, they would find support at MCMC.

Finally, patients would be asked if they wanted to designate one of their loved ones as their "care partner," serving as their primary support person during their stay and after discharge.

Care partners were responsible for performing a variety of functions. These ran from serving as the family spokesperson and patient advocate to providing emotional and spiritual support. Care partners also would be trained — if they chose — to perform basic medical procedures, such as changing wound dressings, that could be done at home, saving them money on professional home care and helping reduce the incidence of re-hospitalization.

As with every component of the program, the decision of whether or not to choose a care partner and fully participate in Planetree was left to the patient.

MCMC's new nursing model put the care of a small group of

patients into the hands of a single registered nurse. He or she was responsible for coordinating and overseeing each patient's individualized care plan throughout the hospital stay, deepening the bond between patient and caregiver.

The care-partner coordinator, also a registered nurse, continued to work with patients and their families, assisting with clinical tasks if needed, but also tending to any personal needs of patients. In the MCMC of old (and most other hospitals), patients were expected to put their personal lives on hold during their stay.

Patients were not the only ones reaping the benefits of Planetree. Instead of ending each day exhausted and wondering if they had accomplished anything, MCMC nurses like Bailey and Carson couldn't wait to get home and share stories with their spouses.

"Right after we made the change to Planetree, a Native American patient was admitted who was a well-known storyteller in her tribe," Bailey recalled. "I was combing her hair, while three or four of her family members visited with her. At one point I reached down and pulled her hair out of the comb and was going to drop it in the trash can, and these women told me, 'No, please don't throw it away.'

"This patient had saved all of the hair that had fallen out of her head since she was a child. In her tribal tradition, your hair is used to stuff the pillow you eventually will be buried with. From that day on, we took special care to honor her tradition. Even when we changed the linen on her bed, we would check first to make sure we had collected any hair that had fallen out."

Under Planetree, MCMC nurses felt liberated to perform favors for patients that previously would have been considered a poor use of their limited time or too inconvenient for staff.

When a patient wanted her lunch to be delayed so she could watch her favorite soap opera uninterrupted, food service staff complied. When another Native American patient wanted to set up his totems around his bed, nurses worked around them. When a large family took over one of the family activity rooms for several days to be near their dying mother, MCMC nurses made sure they had plenty of blankets and were comfortable.

"Planetree taught all of us nurses very quickly that people don't remember exactly what you said or did, but they remember how you made them feel," said Carson who, like Bailey, was a primary nurse when Planetree was implemented but later became a care-partner coordinator.

"We learned that patients didn't really care if we give them their shot or hung their antibiotic bag on time. They cared that you took a few extra minutes to let them cry on your shoulder, or that you listened to them when they were worried about who was going to care for their children if they died of cancer."

Planetree made Carson, Bailey and MCMC's other nurses remember why they had entered their profession in the first place. They were disenchanted as nurses before, but almost overnight their love of their profession returned.

Thoughts *from* Leland Kaiser

THE EVER-CHANGING ROLE
OF THE NURSE

Nursing as a profession is moving toward the concept of patient-centered care. In this role, the nurse is more than a clinical caregiver. The nurse may also be a confidant, a mentor, a teacher, a spiritual guide, a healer, a family relations expert, an advocate for the patient and a person knowledgeable in community resources.

This is quite an order for a nurse trained in a traditional nursing school. And not just nursing is involved in this evolving definition of nursing care. The attitudes and training of physicians also play a major role. Physicians must support the expanded role of nursing and view nurses as true patient-care partners. Some doctors are ready for this redefinition of nursing, and others are not.

We live in a world of our own creation. Everything that is "out there," we put out there. That is why a change of consciousness changes our world. We create the reality we live in.

An important skill for healthcare managers is learning to change their consciousness and the consciousness of their organization and community. When a hospital owns the sickness in its community, it can set about transforming that sickness into wellness. You can transform only what you own. If you see community disease as outside yourself, you empower its hold over you and you are powerless to change it.

Our first challenge is to escape the "consensus reality" of our time and culture. A kind of mass hypnosis holds our consensual reality in place. Compare our situation with the witch trials of an earlier century. The people's shared beliefs in witches created a shared reality experienced by both the witches and the persecutors.

The same is true today. What is going on in our healthcare industry is simply a function of our shared beliefs. If we believe in a scarcity of resources, we act in such a way that we create the expected shortage. If we believe there is enough to go around, we share our resources with one another and enjoy a resulting abundance.

We should have a national conversation about the kind of reality we wish to experience in healthcare and then set about making it happen. This is called a designer reality. Reality then becomes not fate, but intention. Such is the destiny of the healthcare leaders who will follow us in this century. Understanding that you are a reality creator takes a long time. Once you do, you stop trying to adjust to consensus reality and begin to design your own personal reality.

Mark was not managing within the reality he was given. Mark precipitated a new reality. He began managing reality itself. This was not an exercise in accommodation. It was an exercise in radical change.

Mark worked intensively with his medical staff, as well as with overly cautious individual physicians. He also worked with members of nursing administration. In addition, Mark set up an extensive nurse-training program as part of the corporate university at MCMC.

Mark had to take a full-throttle approach to move ahead in this difficult arena. Some caregivers at MCMC hoped Mark would fail. Most understood what he was trying to do. They applauded his efforts and supported him, particularly when the going got rough.

Fortunately, Mark had the support of his board, as well as most of the physicians and nurses and important members of the community. Otherwise, this would have been a grand idea that never got off the ground. More than once, Mark put his job on the line to accomplish a strategic objective.

Make no mistake: This type of changeover has heavy political ramifications. It is not a good place for the faint of heart. Mark often played the game of double or nothing. If you visit MCMC, you will see that Mark ended up on the double side of his career gamble.

CHAPTER 7

A STORY WORTH TELLING

By the time journalist Bill Moyers arrived in The Dalles in April 1992 with a television production crew in tow, Mid-Columbia Medical Center was officially a Planetree hospital stem-to-stern.

The open house that would introduce the hospital's stunning new physical and philosophical makeover to those who hadn't already experienced it as patients was still several weeks away. But MCMC's employees, physicians, nurses, volunteers and even board members were already putting into practice the tenets that Mark Scott had first heard about three years earlier.

As he guided MCMC's transformation, Scott sometimes wondered if the moment when Planetree went live would ever arrive. Never long on patience, he felt that the three years needed to implement the new program were about two-and-a-half years too long.

Turning a hospital inside out; changing the mindset of 600 employees and an entire medical staff; completely reorganizing a healthcare delivery system; remodeling a hospital in a very nonhospital way; gutting an old house and rebuilding it as a comprehensive health library — each aspect of the Planetree implementation was a major initiative in itself. And, of course, through it all there was still the matter of running a hospital.

A transformation this complete ought to take time, and Scott, his board and key leaders throughout the organization had been determined to do it right.

Had Scott needed more validation that this project was something truly special, the presence of Moyers and his film crew provided it.

Moyers was interviewing patients and staff for inclusion in an upcoming series for PBS television called "Healing and the Mind." To Scott, sitting in a comfortable stuffed chair in his hospital's beautiful atrium and preparing for his interview with Moyers, everything felt exactly right.

The PBS series would not air until almost a year later, in February 1993. By that time, the bold experiment under way at MCMC was garnering significant attention. The regional media and industry trades were the first to take notice, but soon the general media were developing stories around the growing number of hospitals that were espousing a more patient-centered approach to healthcare delivery. Planetree often was included as one of the industry's new innovators, and with its hospital-wide implementation, MCMC offered the perfect photo opportunity.

While Moyers and his crew interviewed and filmed at the hospital, the small local daily, *The Dalles Chronicle*, ran an exhaustive 10-part series on the Planetree implementation.

"We need to go back to where healthcare started," Scott told the paper. "We've been focused on technology and physicians and nurses, and that's all been good, but this industry has forgotten the patients to a certain degree. Planetree reawakened us to that fact."

The paper captured the excitement of hospital staff and physicians on the eve of Planetree's implementation. "I think it's going to be the best thing that ever happened to this hospital," said an MCMC medical records employee.

A hospital pathologist demonstrated the effectiveness of Scott's training efforts when he told the paper, "I think this is a great idea. The educational component of Planetree is very important. The more knowledge patients have about their medical problem, the better they'll feel. If I or someone in my family had to be hospitalized, this is the kind of hospital I would want to be in."

A few miles west, Portland's major business publication, *The Business Journal*, caught wind of the unusual activities at MCMC and wrote, "From bringing in musicians, storytellers and other live entertainment to a well-stocked video and relaxation tape library, Mid-Columbia tries to make a stay in the hospital a little less stressful. A massage therapist gives neck and back rubs to ease the nerves of people scheduled for surgery.

Every floor has a kitchen and, if their diet permits, patients can have a family member make a home-cooked meal. And with artwork hanging on the walls and a homelike décor, Mid-Columbia looks more like a hotel than a hospital."

Soon, MCMC was getting the attention of media outside the immediate area. *Hospitals*, a leading industry trade magazine, wrote that "Scott's passion for the Planetree model — a revisionary approach to healthcare that places personalized patient care, not technology, at the forefront of health delivery — stems from his belief that 'we're here to treat people correctly in this business.' He says everyone he knows has had some negative experience to relate about a hospital or physician's office visit."

Another industry magazine, *Trustee*, praised the Planetree concept and predicted it would help spur a transformation of the hospital industry. "The real benefit of the Planetree model is its attitude and philosophy — that patients are worth something, that they have brains and can think independently and that if we involve them in their healthcare, we will get better results. Planetree's goal is the move of the '90s and will be the move into the next century in terms of healthcare."

After visiting MCMC for the first time, Leland Kaiser, Ph.D., a healthcare futurist (and co-author of this book) praised the hospital's effort to break age-old, safe design conventions to create a true healing environment.

"The current analogy for hospitals is hospital as automotive repair shop," Kaiser wrote in his newsletter *Healing Healthcare*. "Patients drive in, are fixed and drive out. The vehicle is repaired; the driver is ignored. To design the hospital as a healing space, you must employ additional analogies, such as hospital as home, hospital as cathedral, hospital as theater or hospital as school.

"Healthcare institutions should be wombs — nurturing places that facilitate the growth and development of their occupants...places like Mid-Columbia Medical Center in The Dalles."

Moyers' series aired on PBS on February 22 – 24, 1993, providing an array of perspectives on the mind-body connection. Moyers visited China to explore the "mystery" of Chi, which is based on the idea that all parts of a human being can penetrate and affect one another. He reported on research efforts to understand the links between the brain's activity and that of the immune system. Moyers profiled scientists like Herbert Benson, M.D., of Harvard University Medical School, whose research had shown that meditation could produce physiological and psychological balance, which could in turn lower high blood pressure, decrease the level of chronic pain and diminish the nausea that accompanies chemotherapy.

And Moyers visited a small, rural hospital in Oregon to explore the idea that people with illnesses could achieve better outcomes when the people caring for them not only attended to their medical problems, but also ministered to their mental and emotional states.

The following is the complete transcript of that program.

"Healing and the Mind with Bill Moyers"

Bill Moyers (narrator): I've had occasion in my life, like many of you, to be grateful for technological marvels of modern medicine like CAT scans, MRIs or this angiogram machine here in Inglewood Hospital in New Jersey. None of us would want to be without these when we really need them. But at the same time, there are some things that these advanced technologies simply cannot do. They cannot make you feel like a person; they cannot hold your hand; they cannot take you into their confidence and make you a partner in your own recovery.

This difference is important because research in mind-body medicine shows us that our emotional state affects our vulnerability to disease and how we recover from illness. Our grandmothers knew that, so did [my old family doctor] in my hometown in Texas. When I was sick in bed, even with the measles, his very arrival seemed to make me recover faster.

In this program, we'll see how some doctors in hospitals

are trying to retrieve that healing presence. They've found that if patients are made to feel better, they will often get better. That's what happens when the science of medicine joins the art of healing.

In northern Oregon, far from the streets of Dallas, there is a glimpse of what the future of medical care could be. Here along the banks of the Columbia River, a whole new vision of hospitals is taking shape. The people who live here are practical and conservative. They make their living from orchards, ranching and timber. For medical care, they go to a hospital in a town called The Dalles. It is typical of good, small-town hospitals and is thoroughly state-of-the-art. But for the people who run it, though, the best technology is not enough.

Mark Scott: When you come to the hospital, you're scared; you're sick; you're frightened; you're in pain — all of those things are running through your emotions. Hospitals are cold; they're intimidating; they are very impersonal institutions from a patient's perspective.

(Moyers narrating): Mark Scott is the president of Mid-Columbia Medical Center.

Scott: The environment does enhance the well-being of our patients and of our staff.

Moyers: You think the anxiety I feel as a patient, even as a visitor, affects me medically?

Scott: Absolutely, it's part of the healing process. Curing patients is not just a matter of stapling, suturing, bandaging and sending them home; there's more to medicine than that. There's more to the healing process than the technological end of healthcare.

(Narration): In the fall of 1991, Scott began a major building program, but he wanted more that just a renovated and expanded physical plant.

Scott: What we are putting ourselves through here isn't just a focus of creating a prettier, nicer, less institutional-looking facility. But to acknowledge the fact that the physical environment begins that healing process mentally for that patient and the family members. It brings out those inner resources that will assist in the recovery process.

(Narration): In April of 1992, the new hospital was completed.

Scott: We've spent a lot of time healing a lot of them. We have healthcare that's second to none in this world. We haven't forgotten about the soul, healing the soul. The arts play a very important role in what we are doing here. Classical pieces of music, storytelling, something as simple as story time to take people out of this environment — out of the pain and suffering and healing and smell — and put them into a story. Part of what we are doing here is to give our patients a little bit of relief, a little bit of relaxation mentally as well as physically. And the piano begins to do that.

Moyers: What you're talking about is the acknowledgment that laughter, humor, wit, feeling good is now being recognized as a part of medicine.

Scott: Hippocrates knew that. The father of medicine knew that. And to a certain degree, we've drifted away from it. He knew that worked; that's one of the things that helped people get better.

Moyers: Healing the soul, he said, is as important as healing the body.

Scott: It's equal. One of the reasons we are offering massage therapy is to relax patients so they can be calm in this very tense environment. Going to surgery is the most tense and frightening experience in most people's lives. Giving a simple back or neck massage to relax these people prior to going to surgery is something we feel is very, very helpful in the healing process.

(Narration): Like nurses everywhere, the nurses here perform the familiar duties of modern medicine. But they do more; they are also the midwives to healing. Nurses like Sue Kelly work hard at understanding the patients' emotional needs. The right human contact, they believe, speeds the patient's recovery. Sometimes it's as simple as holding a patient's hand.

Sue Kelly: Years ago, if I was found, caught, at the bedside holding a patient's hand and doing nothing but that, it would be considered a waste of time because there were tasks and things to do and patients were "diseases." And they were "surgeries," or were "hips," or "fractured femurs." But the personalities, the essence of the person, was pretty much ignored.

(Narration): Sometimes, it's not just the hand that needs touching, but the spirit.

Kelly: Finally, this is everything I ever wanted. Medicine is everything that it should be.

(Narration): Tia Bailey has been a nurse for over 20 years.

Tia Bailey: What I'm here for is to take care of my patient, whatever that entails. If my patient needs me to sit down for 30 minutes with them instead of maybe being out at my desk where someone can see me, maybe charting, that's fine. The rest of it gets done, but the patient comes first. Whenever I do that, I don't feel like I'm going to get in trouble; I feel like I'm going to get praised.

Moyers: How much reckoning do you give to the emotions of the patients?

Kelly: A lot.

Bailey: A lot.

Moyers: To my fear, my anxiety — why?

Bailey: It determines your pain control. If you are afraid, if you are mad, if you are upset about something, whenever I try to deliver analgesia to you, you're not going to get the benefit that you would if I had made you comfortable in your position in your physical surroundings. If I had delivered myself to you as someone who really cares if this Demerol is really going to help you or not. And someone who's going to come back and check on you and say, "Did it help?" And if it didn't, "Let's try something else."

Moyers: Are you saying that my negative emotions can thwart or frustrate the positive effect of medication?

Both: Yes, they can.

Kelly: And it could prevent you from understanding the teaching that we are trying to tell you or what your doctor is saying if your anxiety level is sky-high and you're afraid and you have no one to vent your fear and no one to reassure you. [Then the doctor] comes in, and he tells you, "This and this and this and this is what the x-rays and CAT scans show," and you don't have a clue what he just said, because of your anxiety level. He might as well be speaking in Chinese.

(Narration): One of the most guarded secrets in medicine is the personal medical chart — available to only doctors and nurses, but forbidden to patients.

Kelly: Here we share the chart with the patient, which is a totally unheard-of event. The patient is encouraged to read the chart. You can read it yourself, and we will explain it to you. We shouldn't be the keeper of the knowledge about you. This whole thing is about choices and sharing, about teaching and learning. Teaching you whatever it is you want to know about your body. You have a right to know. You also have the right not to know if you don't want to; you don't have to read your chart. It's about choices.

Moyers: What's the purpose or strategy?

Bailey: Have you ever tried to fight an enemy you don't know? Most people who are sick want information but don't know how to get it. We can provide that information to them.

Moyers: Do you see patients to whom it actually makes a difference to be actively involved?

Kelly: Oh, definitely. If their families are involved, it makes a tremendous difference.

(Narration): Most hospitals with rigid visiting hours especially restrict the comings and goings of children. At Mid-Columbia, though, there are no visiting hours at all. Children are welcome at any time. And there is a pullout bed in every room if a family member wishes to spend the night.

Kelly: Traditionally, we have kept family members way at bay. You can just visit; you can just bring the cards and the flowers — and leave as soon as possible. Visiting hours are now over, and this kind of stuff. That's not what the patient needs; that's not the way it should be. The patient needs the family. If the patient needs the family to be there, the family needs to be there. Oftentimes, the family needs to be there, but they're scared. They need to have the teaching; they need to have the nurturing of the nurses, too.

(Narration): The healing power of a meal provided by familiar hands is a part of folk wisdom. Mid-Columbia provides a kitchen on every floor and encourages family members to prepare meals that would be emotionally nourishing.

Scott: Being in this hospital is a traumatic experience; we are trying to soften that as much as we can. To try to humanize this experience if that's possible.

Moyers: What you're describing is a circle of healing, that is, this physical environment, my state of mind as a patient and the state of my body are all related.

Scott: All tied together, and we're pulling all of those pieces back together. We haven't achieved it to our level of satisfaction. But at least we're working on it. At least we are focused on bringing those pieces back together the best that we can in this small, little hospital in this little, small part of the country. We are trying our darnedest to allow those pieces to begin to come back together.

Before "Healing and the Mind" aired, much of the healthcare industry had become familiar with MCMC. After the series aired, much of the rest of the world took notice. "Healing and the Mind" scored ratings almost double PBS's usual numbers for the time of year, and an accompanying book soared to the top of best-seller lists.

MCMC's switchboard lit up like a Christmas tree with calls from hospital administrators, far-off patients and hundreds of others who wanted to learn more about this new concept in caring.

Thoughts from Leland Kaiser

THE CEO AS A VISIONARY

An important source of Mark Scott's power at MCMC was the contagious power of his vision. He wanted to provide a new and better type of patient care — care that honored the patient, involved the patient and provided healing experiences for the patient and family. He wanted MCMC to reach out and heal its community. He envisioned a community hospital that actually improved the health status of its community.

Mark's vision was a very powerful and atypical vision in the hospital industry. It was an attempt at a radical redefinition of what a community hospital should be, what it should do and how it should go about its business. He communicated this vision with clarity and passion and thereby enrolled many other people in its fulfillment.

Because visions are about the future, Mark of necessity became a futurist — not just a run-of-the-mill futurist, but an activist futurist. He had ideas about how the future of healthcare ought to look, and he wanted to implement those ideas. This put him squarely in the action arena. His interest was not academic. It was nitty-gritty, pushy and practical.

Anyone can guess about the future. Mark decided to create it at MCMC. He didn't know he couldn't possibly do it, so he did it. Anyone can guess about the future, and some futurists guess quite well. However, inventing the future is more important than attempting to predict it. The good futurist is a self-fulfilling prophet. He or she prognosticates a preferable future and then hurries to fulfill his or her own prediction. Self-fulfilling prophecy is futurism at its best. This was Mark's variety of futurism.

Here is a simple definition of a vision. A vision is:

- The best thing you can imagine happening.
- A comprehensive description of a future condition you want to create.

- An image of the future.
- A prized possibility set in future time.
- Your hoped-for destination.
- An expression of your personal values and aspirations.

It is important to remember that a vision consists of images, pictures or graphic representations. It is not just a set of words, as in a mission statement. If you use words at all to describe a vision, you should create a word picture perceived by the right side of the brain.

Often, when people talk about having a vision, they are using the word as simply another term for a written statement. Visioning is the process of generating and sharing images. One vivid picture is worth a thousand words, as the old admonition goes.

Images inspire us. They constitute the natural language of the brain.

The vision of your healthcare organization is a vivid picture of its future condition, such as you would see if you walked through it and simply described what you saw happening.

The visionary understands the interconnected fabric of reality. This permits him to perceive existing and potential linkages among the components of the universe. Often, a vision is simply a new way of linking components together.

Contemporary healthcare organizations need to build safe harbors for their visionaries. Visioning proceeds best in a supportive environment where the rules have been altered to permit innovation, creativity and discovery. Of course, accountability is still present.

At some point, the visionary must bring back something of value to his sponsoring organization, as Mark did. There must be accountability in visioning, but it is not measured by the time clock. It is the accountability of better organizational outcomes generated through the visioning process.

CHAPTER 8

MATTERS OF THE MIND

After only a few months in practice at Mid-Columbia Medical Center, Planetree clearly was going to become a long-term success. Staff at every level had embraced the tenets of the new model of care. Already, Planetree was becoming second nature. MCMC staff had stopped practicing it and were now living it.

Physicians had accepted the changes they were required to make in their practice patterns — most of them enthusiastically. A few old-school physicians were slower to completely buy into the notion of open medical records, patients asking questions and "warm-and-fuzzy" storytellers — on the patient care team, of all things.

Still, there were no outward revolts, no stubborn refusals to participate. Scott hadn't had a Planetree-related run-in with a physician since an enraged doctor had stormed into his office demanding to know why his patient could get information about a complementary therapy so easily.

In fact, while Planetree was being planned and before its first year had passed, Scott was able to recruit six new physicians to his medical staff — never an easy task for a small-town hospital administrator. Each of them indicated that the hospital's Planetree philosophy contributed to his or her decision to relocate to The Dalles.

In Planetree's first several months, the degree of participation varied widely among patients and their families. Many dove enthusiastically into the program; others sampled one or more components. Many opted out of participating altogether, preferring to receive their care the old-fashioned way.

Whether or not they chose to participate in Planetree's offerings, all MCMC patients now were experiencing a benefit not available in many other American hospitals: the freedom to choose.

Only three years earlier, Scott had been on the verge of a career change, burned out by healthcare in general. Now, Planetree was his crowning achievement as a CEO. It had reenergized him, and now that it was up and running smoothly, Scott knew that the restless CEO in him would resurface before long. He understood now that his previous dissatisfaction with his career had been due in large part to his disdain for the status quo.

Implementing Planetree throughout an entire hospital was a remarkable accomplishment for Scott and his staff, but it left him even more determined to raise the bar for himself as a leader. Already, he was looking for another challenge. It wouldn't take long to find it.

Bill Moyers' remarkably popular "Healing and the Mind" series had exposed MCMC to an enormous audience. It generated a wave of interest that started the day after the MCMC episode aired and continued heavily for the next few months, and steadily over the next several years.

In addition to more media, scores of hospital representatives from around the world were calling daily to request tours of the first Planetree hospital.[6]

Scott was stunned by the interest, not just in MCMC, but in the entire Moyers series. "Really, the first time I even gave any thought to the mind-body connection in the healing process was when the Moyers film crew came to do some advance work before Bill arrived," Scott said.

"They told me they had been working on the series for three years, traveling all over the world to learn how people of other cultures were using acupuncture and massage therapy and meditation. So, when the series aired and started generating so much attention, a few lightbulbs started going on in my head."

Moyers followed up his series by arranging several conferences around the country that further explored the mind-body connection.

[6]As of December 2007, MCMC had hosted representatives of more than 2,000 hospitals from the United States and numerous other countries.

He invited Scott to participate on panel discussions during several of his stops. In Morristown, New Jersey, Moyers moderated a session featuring Scott and two other gentlemen whose names were unfamiliar to the small-town hospital CEO. On one side was Herbert Benson, M.D., a pioneer in mind-body medicine, who also had been featured in the "Healing and the Mind" series.

On the other side was Larry Dossey, M.D., an internist who was doing groundbreaking work in the area of spirituality and healing.

Scott listened attentively as Benson and Dossey spoke of their unique practices and the results of their clinical research. He found Dossey's discussion of the power of prayer in the healing process "a little too out there, even for me."[7]

But Scott was transfixed by listening to Benson describe how he was using behavioral medicine techniques to integrate the mind and body. Benson was combining standard medical practices with nutrition, education, exercise and something Scott had never heard of — the relaxation response. Benson, the founding president of the Mind/Body Medical Institute at Harvard Medical School, was the first to define the relaxation response, a physiological state of deep rest that reduces stress and anxiety in the mind and the body.

As Scott listened raptly, Benson explained research that indicated that up to 90 percent of all physician visits were for stress-related complaints. Teaching people how to reduce their stress by employing relaxation response techniques had proved effective in treating a range of disorders, from chronic pain to heart disease.

Scott thought back to the first time he had heard Robin Orr and realized this was another seminal moment in his career. Morristown was his new Pajaro Dunes. "I remember thinking, I should be in the stress management business," Scott said.

Soon enough, he would be. With Planetree now fully operational at MCMC, Scott believed he had laid the perfect foundation for a mind-body medicine program. Soon after he returned to The Dalles, Scott set

---

[7] It wouldn't be for long. The next chapter explores Scott's integration of spirituality into MCMC's patient care philosophy.

up a visit to Benson's Mind/Body Institute in Boston.

When he and a group of key staff members returned from that visit, Scott was determined to build his own mind-body center at MCMC, borrowing ideas from Benson but developing many of the program components from scratch.

Again, Scott knew the success of another nontraditional medical program would require buy-in from his medical staff. He had to identify another champion to help sell the concept. This time it had to be a physician, someone so completely behind the concept that he or she would agree to serve as the medical director of the new institute.

Scott had no idea where he was going to find that person. But as it turned out, the person he needed was already looking for him.

In the late 1980s, Steve McLennon, M.D., was fresh out of medical school, into his family medicine training and stressed close to the breaking point.

"I wasn't doing a very good job of taking care of myself," McLennon said. "Being a young doctor was hard work. The hours were long; there was a lot to learn; and you had the responsibility of keeping schedules. I didn't recognize how it might be impacting me."

Others did. McLennon was practicing in the department of family medicine at St. Joseph's Hospital in Chicago, and one patient kept returning to his clinic for no apparent reason.

"There was nothing really wrong with her other than that she was 89 and had the usual issues that come with age," McLennon said. "I was kind of whining to my supervisor one day about her, saying, 'She comes in week-after-week, and there's really nothing I can do for her.' And this doctor told me, 'She must be getting something from you; otherwise she wouldn't be coming.' I remember thinking, 'Well, that's a different concept.' One day this woman came in and handed me a pamphlet. And up at the top, printed in jagged letters, it read 'How to Deal with Stress.'

"I thought, Oh, I'm not stressed. You're the hypochondriac, crazy person. But I can sure use this. I'll copy it and give it to all those stressed patients I see on a daily basis. This sweet lady gave me an opportunity to take a look at myself, but I ignored it. I carried that pamphlet around for years and would often give it to my patients. But I never read it myself."

As McLennon got deeper into his medical practice, his symptoms became harder to ignore. He developed back pain that grew serious enough that once or twice a week he was unable to get out of bed to go to work. One physician friend thought it was a herniated disk; another colleague suspected stress.

"I didn't like the idea that it was a herniated disk, but that was better than thinking it was related to stress," McLennon said. "I mean, this was my life. This is what I had worked for. I had debt. I couldn't just quit and move to the beach."

Instead, McLennon moved to The Dalles. In 1991, he joined the MCMC medical staff, one of the six physicians who came on board during the planning and implementation of Planetree. "I'm not sure I fully understood Planetree at the time, but what I knew about it certainly fit my philosophy more than what I was practicing at the large medical center," he said.

McLennon joined a small family-practice group and started seeing patients, believing he had left his stress 2,000 miles behind him. His back was feeling better. He loved his new community. The young doctor and his wife were expecting their first child, and they had adapted quickly to the small-town quality of life The Dalles offered.

But before long, the demands of McLennon's rapidly growing practice began taking a toll. He was working long hours in his clinic and had taken on additional responsibilities on the MCMC medical staff. The stress at work was causing stress at home. McLennon's relationship with his wife was suffering, and he worried that his new child, though a blessing, also would be just one more person wanting a piece of him.

"I was just burning out," McLennon said. "I hit the wall when my wife told me she didn't know what to do anymore; she didn't know if she could stay with me."

McLennon was devastated. He went into a deep depression, going several months without getting a full night's sleep. He lost 30 pounds. Earlier, McLennon had made a decision to pursue a degree in spiritual psychology from the University of Santa Monica. In spite of his emotional state, he followed through with his original plan and enrolled in the program. It couldn't have come at a better time.

"Through that process, I started to become aware of sensations in my body other than back pain. I learned to listen to myself and found out I really wasn't that bad off. It was a very important turning point for me to learn to have some access to my emotions, and to learn to express them."

The experience carried over into McLennon's practice, and he developed an interest in aspects of his patients' health other than their physical state.

"I realized that a lot of the people who were coming to see me every day were not having physical problems as much as were dealing with issues related to lifestyle or stress, or a general lack of contentment," he said.

McLennon started reading books that addressed the mind-body connection, including *Minding the Body, Mending the Mind*, written by Joan Borysenko, Ph.D., a colleague of Dr. Benson at Harvard. McLennon's interest in the mind's role in the healing process deepened.

Although none of the stress-inducing factors in his life had changed, McLennon was feeling better than he had in years. He was teaching himself how to cope with stress better. It took him a while to recognize how significantly stress had been affecting his own life, but now that he understood, he could easily identify the signs of it in his own patients.

Teaching stress management techniques had become an important component of his personal patient-care philosophy. Seeing the positive results in his own health and that of many of his patients, he started feeling like a "stress management evangelist," anxious to share what he was learning with colleagues and virtually anyone else who would listen.

When he heard about the MCMC team members who had just returned from a visit to the Mind/Body Institute at Harvard, McLennon, now familiar with Benson's work, sensed a golden opportunity.

Throughout the implementation of Planetree, fate had so often smiled on Scott that he never had a moment of doubt in his decision to take such a bold step. Every component of the program was so new that the odds were slim he'd find experienced people to run them and ensure their success. Yet every time he went looking for someone smart and experienced enough to lead a program or passionate enough to champion it, those individuals virtually fell in his lap — Bill Hamilton and Robert Staver helping convert the MCMC medical staff; Randy Carter catching Scott's attention in the hospital lab and blossoming into Planetree's articulate spokesman and trainer; Michele Spatz happening upon a help-wanted ad and moving across the country to build the Planetree Health Resource Center.

And now Scott, proceeding with plans to build MCMC's own Center for Mind and Body Medicine before he had identified a medical director, was listening to his secretary tell him Dr. Steve McLennon would like a moment of his time.

"I had just finished Joan Borysenko's book when I heard that Mark had taken a group of people to visit Herb Benson's Mind/Body Institute," McLennon said. "I went into Mark's office the next day and said, 'If you're planning to start a mind-body center here and you need a physician involved, I'm your man.'"

Neither Scott nor McLennon were ideally qualified to direct the development of MCMC's own mind-body center, which would be the first of its kind west of the Mississippi. But Scott knew they had a lot going for them anyway. Foremost was the foundation of Planetree that was already in place.

"We were stepping into an area none of us knew much about," Scott said. "But we knew a lot of good research had been done to quantify the benefits of this approach. And, with Planetree, we had already gone over the hurdle of introducing complementary medicine into a traditional medical model."

Scott named McLennon as his medical director and sent him and several staff members to Boston to train under Benson and the Mind/Body Institute staff. They focused much of their attention on learning how to teach patients relaxation response techniques, which would be incorporated into all of the MCMC center's core programs.

Scott's plan was to build his mind-body center around a foundation of three traditional medical programs — cardiac rehabilitation, pulmonary rehabilitation, diabetes management — and a fourth, medical symptom reduction, which would be devoted to teaching stress management to people with chronic pain. The medical programs would combine traditional treatments with stress management lessons and techniques, such as yoga, meditation, massage, tai chi and, eventually, acupuncture.

Following Benson's model, the medical symptom reduction program centered on teaching a technique called "mindfulness meditation." Through mindfulness, patients would learn how to have "moment-to-moment awareness of the present," helping them avoid being on "automatic pilot," focused on the past or anxiously awaiting the future. Mindfulness was intended to enable people to respond rather than react to situations and to cultivate a greater sense of calm and well-being.

Benson also espoused integrating the medical and mind-body approaches with exercise and nutrition education, and a new fitness center would be part of MCMC's new mind-body center. Of course, it would be the nicest in town.

As MCMC's key staff were being trained, construction began on the new center. The facility would be located in the medical office complex Scott had constructed 50 yards from the hospital atrium. The first floor housed MCMC University and a conference room. Several physicians had offices upstairs, but Scott had left one space a shell while waiting for the right tenant. Now he had it.

In another stroke of Scott's continued good fortune, a Hood River orchardist heard of MCMC's plans to construct a mind-body center and made an anonymous $350,000 donation to help fund the project.

The Center for Mind and Body Medicine was unveiled during a public open house on November 8, 1996. Like Planetree before it, the new center was promoted not so much as a bold new idea but as ancient practices being put to work in a modern context. Two thousand years earlier, Aristotle had postulated that the mind was nothing more than a bodily function. The new Center for Mind and Body Medicine was a place where that theory would be merged with the wonders of modern medicine to provide more thorough healing opportunities for patients.

Staff of the new center took great pains to avoid referring to the less-traditional components of the center's programs as "alternative" medicine. Not only was the word poison to most physicians, but it also wasn't accurate. Yoga, tai chi, meditation and breathing techniques were merely tools to "complement" traditional therapy. They weren't intended to replace anything.

With McLennon supervising the medical components of the center, Scott needed someone to oversee the administrative component. Again, he knew he wasn't likely to find anyone classically trained to run a mind-body center. Instead, he'd be looking for someone with enough smarts, passion and general management skills to overcome a lack of experience in such a unique setting. Given that a laboratory technician would wind up being Scott's Planetree trainer, no one was surprised when Scott chose a former pharmacist to run his mind-body center.

Dianne Storby came to MCMC Planetree-ready. She joined the hospital just two months after the Center for Mind and Body Medicine was opened, moving from a small hospital in the Samaritan Health System (now Banner Health) in Arizona. In 1994, during a medical conference in Scottsdale, Storby had attended a breakout session on Planetree that Scott was leading. She'd never heard of him or the program, but Storby figured it had to be more entertaining than another discussion of managed care. She never guessed it would be life-changing.

"I was a clinical pharmacist by training, and I liked to think I was fairly good," said Storby. "But I always judged my self-worth by how good I was at anticipating physicians' needs, having something there for them before they even asked for it. Patients and family weren't my priority; making doctors happy was. As I sat and listened to Mark describe Planetree, I actually started crying. I realized my perspective was 180-degrees off. It became my mission to get my hospital to implement Planetree."

After convincing a group of executives to visit Planetree, Storby succeeded not only in selling Planetree to her own hospital, but also to every other hospital in the Samaritan Health System. The achievement wasn't lost on Scott, who was looking for a new pharmacy director at the same time he was opening his mind-body center. Storby initially turned down the job offer, thinking it was a step down from her administrative position with Banner. Ultimately, the opportunity was too appealing to refuse.

It wasn't long after Storby joined Scott's team that she learned, like so many MCMC employees before her, that her job description was only to be used as a general guideline. In addition to running the hospital pharmacy, Storby soon found herself in charge of several other MCMC programs, including the new mind-body center.

"I could immediately see a burning desire and tenacity in Dianne that convinced me she was able to take on a challenge like this," Scott said.

Storby embraced the opportunity to direct a program that added so many new tools to the traditional treatment of common diseases. And she relished the challenge of selling physicians on the idea of approaching with open minds the notion that their patients would be introduced to an array of complementary techniques to enhance their healing.

But, again, many of those battles already had been fought and won during the Planetree implementation. Even Scott's decision to formally credential acupuncturists and grant them admission to the MCMC medical staff met with surprisingly little opposition from physicians.

"We were well-prepared to address what we figured would be a lot of physician concerns," Scott said. "We pulled together reams of data that quantified the benefits of acupuncture and let the physicians know it was available to them. But the more we talked to them, the more we realized this wasn't going to be a big deal.

"A lot of the doctors had testimonials about using acupuncture themselves or knew people who had benefited from it. When it came time for the physicians to vote on whether or not acupuncture would be recognized as a specialty on the MCMC medical staff, the vote was unanimous in favor of it."

If there were any concerns about patients accepting the mind-body concepts, those vanished as soon as the center opened. Again, patients always had the option to choose the traditional approaches to caring for their heart or lung disease, diabetes or chronic pain. But Scott, Storby and staff were delighted to see so many members of their conservative, agriculture-based community at least willing to try yoga or meditation, even tai chi and aromatherapy. And the massage therapy that was introduced to so many offerings of the mind-body center was a universal hit.

Again, in his determination to continue transforming the healthcare experience for patients and their families, Scott had rolled the dice and won.

Thoughts *from* Leland Kaiser

HOW A CHANGE OF WORLD VIEW CHANGES THE WORLD VIEWED

We gaze at the universe through our window (world view or paradigm) and then mistake the universe for the window. If through chance or good fortune, we get a glimpse of the universe through a larger window (new paradigm), it appears to have undergone an immense expansion.

The visionary simply views the universe through a larger window. He sees more than small-window people. The vision that appears in a large window often looks scary, evil, unearthly or impractical to people still stuck in small windows. The visionary is in a quandary. Should he try to increase the window size of his peers or reduce the size of his vision to fit their existing windows? In religious terms, do we try to reduce the mind of God to fit our size or expand our minds to reach toward His size?

It is safe to assume the world is never as it appears to be. It is always much larger. The common-sense view necessarily misses the mark. This is best illustrated in quantum physics, where the viewer's window is so large it refutes most of what he has been trained to accept as common-sense reality.

Since the visionary sees through a large window but lives in a small-window world, he is always frustrated. How can he make his visions practical and understandable to others? Should he break down his vision into a progressive series of smaller snapshots and slowly lead his viewers from one picture to the other? Should he remain silent about the larger view and be seen by others as sane and in touch with reality?

A visionary is always pushing the edges of the current envelope and is always in danger of falling off the edge. We see this in the life of Nikola Tesla, who enjoyed such an immense view of the universe that scientists are still trying to bring his vision within range of their windows.

Until you doubt conventional wisdom, you will not change windows. With doubt about the size of your existing window come fear and a loss of security provided by the old, more comfortable views. This is why most people stay glued to their current windows. They are afraid of seeing more and losing the security provided by their old views.

A vision challenges old ways of being, seeing and doing. People ready for transformation eagerly grasp the new vision. It frees and liberates them. People not ready for change resist the vision and vilify the visionary. They believe the old ways are best and seek to prevent the new.

The visionary must be able to accept both types of people and avoid discounting those individuals not yet ready to grow. They are still in their protective cocoons of old beliefs and traditions. They must sleep a while longer before they are willing to emerge into the dawning light of a new day with yet greater possibilities.

I often tell healthcare managers, "What you need for the next few years is not a good pen, but a big eraser." We have so many lines (boundaries) drawn in this industry that it is barely possible to move among them. Whether those boundaries are licensure, antitrust or gender bias, they limit our freedom to act in new ways. Visionaries like Mark Scott challenge us to "imagine the world without the lines."

CHAPTER 9

SPIRITUALITY AND HEALING

"Medicine and religion have worked hand in hand in the process of healing for thousands of years. In ancient societies (as in some less-developed societies today), illness was perceived as primarily a spiritual problem...

"From the early Christian era through the Reformation, the relationship between medicine and religion remained close. The first hospitals were founded in monasteries, and the missionary movement linked physical healing with spiritual conversion.

"By the 17th century, rifts between medicine and religion emerged, because of the challenges of church authorities and the rise of empirical science. Science claimed the body (and later the mind) as its purview, while religion held onto the soul. Critiques of religion arose.

"By the late 20th century, a growing disillusionment with the limitations of science again opened up the possibility of a rapprochement between medicine and religion, the twin traditions of healing."

– Dale Matthews, M.D., F.A.C.P.

Among the many lessons Mark Scott learned from the success of Planetree and the Center for Mind and Body Medicine was the value of maintaining an open mind. Never again would Scott underestimate the willingness of patients to attempt something new if it had the potential for improving their health. Not after seeing the traffic in the Planetree Health Resource Center continue to grow dramatically; not after witnessing an 80-year-old lifelong farmer practicing yoga to help alleviate the symptoms of chronic lung disease.

Several months before opening the Center for Mind and Body Medicine, when Scott had been introduced to Dr. Herb Benson and his work integrating the human mind into the healing process, he also had heard Dr. Larry Dossey speak on the role of spirituality in healing. At the time, Dossey's subject failed to strike a chord. But once the mind-body center was up and running successfully, Scott was ready to tackle a new intellectual challenge.

In Scott's mind, Planetree represented a fabulous foundation upon which to develop a truly unique center of healing, and the mind-body center was an ideal "next step," but why stop there? There had to be more.

So in November 1997, Scott and four others from Mid-Columbia Medical Center headed to Los Angeles to attend a conference presented by Benson exploring in-depth the subject of spirituality and medicine.

The keynote speaker was Dale Matthews, M.D., an associate professor of medicine at Georgetown University School of Medicine. Matthews was a practicing internist who incorporated prayer and spirituality into his patient care, and had performed extensive research on their effect on medical outcomes.

The MCMC contingent, which included director of nursing Joyce Powell-Morin and Gretchen Kimsey, a board member (whose husband, Rusty, was bishop of the Eastern Oregon Diocese of the Episcopal Church), heard Matthews present some fascinating statistics from his and other clinical studies.

One study of male medical students showed that the strongest predictor of alcoholism was a lack of religious affiliation. Another indicated that frequent church attendees had lower rates of depression and anxiety. Matthews pointed to a study of patients in a critical care unit indicating that those receiving prayer support had more favorable outcomes than those who did not.

Benson's conference also featured others exploring the role of faith and spirituality in the healing process, including the Rev. Samuel

Solivan, Ph.D., associate professor of Christian theology at Andover Newton Theological School and an adjunct professor at the Harvard Mind/Body Medical Institute.

There was a time when Scott likely would have dismissed such talk as psychobabble, certainly not within the realm of a hospital CEO. Even now, Scott wasn't entirely sure what to make of the statistics he was hearing. But he knew, at the very least, that the role of spirituality in healing was a topic worthy of thoughtful discussion with MCMC staff and physicians, and the timing was right.

In fact, the seeds for a discussion about bringing spirituality to MCMC had actually been sown a few months earlier when Scott had invited a Canadian public health physician named Trevor Hancock, M.D., to speak at MCMC. Hancock, affiliated with the World Health Organization, was a pioneer in the healthy communities movement. Catherine Sessions, the manager whom Scott had put in charge of MCMC's community initiatives, had introduced her CEO to Hancock's writings, especially those pertaining to the role of hospitals in helping to improve the overall well-being of the communities they served.

Hancock's work dealt with the interconnectedness of key elements that contribute to quality of life, a person's physical health being just one element. In fact, Hancock's vision of health described a state not just of biological wellness, but also of social, intellectual, environmental and spiritual well-being.

Scott had used Hancock's visit to launch a new community health enhancement team at MCMC, which was charged with developing or participating in partnerships designed to improve public health. Meeting Hancock also left Scott determined to incorporate the physician's broader definition of health into his ever-expanding vision for MCMC.

Shortly after Hancock's visit, Scott took members of the new community health enhancement team to a conference in San Francisco. While there, the MCMC group visited the Veriditas Labyrinth Project at Grace Cathedral, where thousands of travelers had been drawn over the years to walk two permanent labyrinths.

Scott knew little about labyrinths, which are geometric, sacred walking paths that have existed for more than 3,000 years and have been associated with nearly every major religion. But he had heard of their powers of spiritual renewal and wanted to learn more about them and the Veriditas project.

The project was founded by the Rev. Lauren Artress, who was instrumental in exposing the labyrinth to a modern-day audience. The canon for special ministries at Grace Cathedral, Artress's goal was to see the use of labyrinths expand outside churches to more public environments, including hospitals.

The Mystical Tradition of the Labyrinth

(The following description is excerpted with permisson from the Grace Cathedral website: www.gracecathedral.org.)

The labyrinth is an archetype, a divine imprint, found in all religious traditions in various forms around the world. By walking a replica of the Chartres labyrinth, laid in the floor of Chartres Cathedral in France around 1220, we are rediscovering a long-forgotten mystical tradition that is insisting to be reborn.

The labyrinth has only one path, so there are no tricks to it and no dead ends. The path winds throughout and becomes a mirror for where we are in our lives. It touches our sorrows and releases our joys. Walk it with an open mind and an open heart.

There are three stages of the walk:

• Purgation (Releasing) — A releasing, a letting go of the details of your life. This is the act of shedding thoughts and distractions. A time to open the heart and quiet the mind.

• *Illumination (Receiving) — When you reach the center, stay there as long as you like. It is a place of meditation and prayer. Receive what is there for you to receive.*

• *Union (Returning) — As you leave, following the same path out of the center as you came in, you enter the third stage, which is joining God, your Higher Power or the healing forces at work in the world. Each time you walk the labyrinth, you become more empowered to find and do the work you feel your soul reaching for.*

Guidelines for the walk: Quiet your mind, and become aware of your breath. Allow yourself to find the pace your body wants to go. The path is two ways. Those going in will meet those coming out. You may "pass" people or let others step around you. Do what feels natural.

"The labyrinth is a wonderful tool for anyone," Artress once said in an interview. "Someone can be highly trained in meditation and get a benefit from it. And people who don't have any spiritual practice whatsoever and haven't even darkened the door of a church can walk into the labyrinth. You don't need a discipline, but as you continue to walk, over time, it helps you develop a discipline of focus. Just simply being mindful of what you need is helpful, like, 'Today's kind of chaotic; I think I'll walk the labyrinth.'"

At Grace Cathedral, Scott and his staff were awed by the beautiful path. Each member of the MCMC contingent reported being uniquely touched by taking a meditative walk to the center and back out again. Immediately, Scott began thinking about how to introduce a labyrinth to MCMC.

Not long after returning to The Dalles, Scott received a call from the pastor of the local First United Methodist Church, the Rev. Adele Hustis, who wanted to stop in for a conversation.

"Adele said, 'You've probably never even heard about labyrinths, but I want to talk to you about them,'" Scott said. "It was just like Steve McLennon stepping forward when I was wondering who was going to direct the mind-body center. Pure serendipity."

Hustis's interest in labyrinths had been piqued by two members of her congregation, David and Helen Duff. The couple had received a book on labyrinths from their daughter, who lived in New York City and had recently taken her first walk on a sacred path. Impressed by the experience, she encouraged her parents to read the book. She also suggested they start promoting the idea for a labyrinth in The Dalles.

The Duffs met with Hustis, and the Methodist Church soon had its own labyrinth, painted on a large tarp. Later, David Duff, an engineer, designed a permanent labyrinth that was painted on the church parking lot.

Those were the first labyrinths in The Dalles, but before long, Scott had the third. In autumn 1997 — around the time he arrived home from the Benson conference armed with statistics illustrating the link between spirituality and health — Scott purchased a portable canvas labyrinth and slowly began to introduce it to his staff and community.

"We kept it in the conference room of our medical office building," remembered Powell-Morin, whom Scott designated as MCMC's labyrinth facilitator. "We would roll it out regularly and encourage staff to use it. Then we started scheduling different classes and programs around it. We'd hold our breast-cancer support groups around it and invite youth groups to walk it. As people from the community started hearing about it, they'd call up and ask if they could come walk it or reserve it for a special event."

One family used MCMC's labyrinth to celebrate a grandfather's 80th birthday. A patient dying of lung cancer made a special request to walk the labyrinth in his final days.

Scott and Powell-Morin quickly realized that MCMC needed a permanent labyrinth. It didn't feel right that something that was affecting people so profoundly should be rolled up and stowed in a closet, used only for special events or upon the request of someone fortunate enough to know it existed.

Scott felt that a new, permanent labyrinth could be the focal point of a much broader spirituality initiative at MCMC. In reality, the hospital was already well down that road. With Planetree and the Center for Mind and Body Medicine, MCMC already was addressing in meaningful ways the biological, intellectual, environmental and social components of "more complete" healing. But Benson's 1997 conference had convinced Scott that it was time for spirituality to become a formal part of MCMC's offerings.

Within a few weeks of returning from the Benson conference, Scott invited members of the local ministerial association to a sit-down discussion. His purpose was to share the information he had been compiling related to spirituality and healing and to invite area clergy to help introduce the concept at MCMC.

Scott, of course, had no intention of forcing spirituality on his staff or patients. Indeed, he wasn't sure how such a personal, often hard-to-define "thing" would be formally integrated into MCMC's offerings. The hospital had a chaplain, a chapel and other quiet spaces for personal reflection and prayer. Local clergy were always welcome to visit patients.

At this point, Scott was not even sure he believed the research that suggested the positive power of prayer and faith in the healing process. But without evidence to the contrary, Scott felt a spirituality initiative was certainly worth pursuing. If there were a chance a patient could benefit from a spiritual component to his or her care, why wouldn't it be openly encouraged?

Buoyed by the support of the local clergy, Scott began exploring ways to introduce spirituality into MCMC's offerings. It would be the final component of his new, more comprehensive definition of health and healthcare.

Scott's next step was to organize a two-day Spirituality and Healing in Healthcare Symposium at MCMC to bring together healthcare professionals and clergy for an "exploration of the role of spirituality in health, healing and well-being."

Held March 26–27, 1998, the conference featured as keynote speakers two men from Scott's ever-expanding network of nontraditional healthcare friends and advisers: Dale Matthews, M.D., and the Rev. Samuel Solivan. Scott also enlisted the help of Michael Stillwater, a music therapist who created personal healing songs for patients and staff of many hospitals.

Scott wasn't sure how local clergy, physicians and other healthcare providers would respond to the conference, but he felt the topic and the research related to spirituality and healing were too important to ignore. It wasn't a new concept; the first hospitals were in churches, and hospitals and religion often have been linked.

But, unlike many hospitals, MCMC had no religious tradition nor affiliation. Scott wasn't looking to officially change that, but at his hospital, personal choice had truly become a sacred tenet. Scott was intent on letting his patients, staff, physicians and community know that spiritual beliefs of all forms would be supported in his hospital.

By all measures, the first-time symposium was a resounding success, drawing more than 150 people not just from the local area but from as far away as New York, Montana and Texas.

"It was clear we had hit a chord," Scott said. "Healthcare professionals were confronted with this complex topic on a regular basis, but they weren't really prepared to be a good resource. People like Matthews and Solivan were presenting some really interesting research on how beliefs influenced healing, but those concepts hadn't been widely accepted in mainstream medicine. We were just trying to help encourage the discussion locally, but the topic had a much broader appeal."

The symposium was so successful that Scott decided to make it a regular event. The second annual symposium was scheduled for November 1999.

In the meantime, MCMC worked to broaden its spirituality initiative. Scott ordered several handmade wooden "finger labyrinths," which were placed throughout the hospital for bed-bound patients or others unable to walk the temporary labyrinth.

Then in spring 1998, Scott and a contingent of MCMC executives, including Powell-Morin; Randy Carter, director of training; and Cheryl Gebhart, human resources director, plus Hustis, the Methodist Church pastor, returned to Grace Cathedral to participate in a labyrinth facilitator-training program.

"Mark was the only hospital administrator there," Powell-Morin remembered. "He was always the only hospital administrator at these sorts of things."

Powell-Morin was particularly taken by the labyrinth's spiritual component. It was hard to learn its history and not be.

"During the Middle Ages, churches placed stone-patterned labyrinths inside their cathedrals," she said. "During the Crusades and Holy Wars, it was dangerous for people to make their pilgrimage to Jerusalem, so the churches built labyrinths to allow people to make symbolic spiritual journeys. They were used in that manner for many years. As time passed, many churches covered their labyrinths with pews, and they were never used again."

During the remodeling project that accompanied MCMC's Planetree conversion, Scott would often remark that the physical makeover was the least important component of Planetree. One of his favorite lines had become, "We could implement Planetree in a M.A.S.H. tent and be successful." Nonetheless, Scott had remodeled the hospital.

As he learned more about the labyrinth, Scott understood that its power was in the experience, not the medium. But after walking the beautiful terrazzo stone labyrinth at Grace Cathedral and learning the history of labyrinths, Scott knew the time had come to replace MCMC's portable canvas labyrinth. He wanted a labyrinth that would one day have its own rich history. He saw the meditative walk as another healing tool in MCMC's unique mix of traditional and nontraditional offerings. Furthermore, a permanent labyrinth at MCMC would be a powerful, visible symbol that spirituality, in its many forms, was embraced here.

And so Scott set about to build it.

As the labyrinth project got underway, Scott put the members of the community health management team to work implementing the next component of MCMC's spirituality initiative: a Parish Nurse program. The goal of the program was to link nurses with local congregations to provide an array of health-related services, primarily in the areas of prevention and education.

"The idea of the Parish Nurse program was to provide a connection between members of churches in our community and resources to help enhance their quality of life," said Powell-Morin. "The local churches provided us with a wonderful network that enabled us to reach a lot of people, many of whom weren't aware of all the important resources available to them."

Parish nurses worked on a voluntary basis, performing blood pressure checks at community meals, leading education programs and providing many other health-related services.

"The Parish Nurse program provided us a way to keep health at the forefront of people's minds and to offer them opportunities to connect with programs and services to help them lead healthier lives," Powell-Morin said. "It helped us get people to think of MCMC as an organization that was actively out in the community partnering to improve community health, rather than just a place concerned about sick people."

In November 1999, MCMC convened its second Spirituality and Healing in Healthcare Symposium. Dale Matthews returned as a keynote speaker, and Michael Stillwater was back with his "Music Medicine."

Topics of sessions again were far from what most were used to hearing at a hospital-sponsored conference: "Recovering the Soul of Medicine: Old Traditions, Sustaining Values and a New Vision;" "The Healing Relationship: Mystery, Wonder and Medicine;" and "Integrated Faith and Prayer Into Healthcare Practice."

Scott's special guest was Lauren Artress, who spoke about the labyrinth as a healing tool and then helped dedicate MCMC's new permanent labyrinth. Made of terrazzo stone and surrounded by a beautiful garden, MCMC's labyrinth was located between the hospital and a medical office building on a site formerly used as a landing pad for emergency transport helicopters.[8]

---

[8]Ironically, the labyrinth would continue to serve as what had to be one of the country's most ornate helicopter landing pads.

The symposium provided the perfect backdrop for the labyrinth dedication, and Scott felt there was no better person to unveil the new feature than Artress, whose work had first introduced Scott to the wondrous structures.

Having the labyrinth ready in time for the symposium had been no small feat. The firm Scott originally hired to construct the labyrinth had no previous experience building such a structure. The finished labyrinth had problems with drainage and cracking. An annoyed Scott had it torn up and went looking for a new contractor.

"I wasn't about to have something that sacred be that flawed," he said.

After a national search — and much to Scott's amazement — a labyrinth construction expert was found in Memphis, Tennessee. This time, MCMC's labyrinth was completed to Scott's exacting specifications.

"The difference was that the first labyrinth was constructed by laborers," Scott said. "But the second one was completed by an artist. This was a mission for him, and he poured his heart into it."

After helping dedicate MCMC's beautiful new labyrinth, Artress led symposium attendees on a meditative walk. As Scott took the one-third mile walk to the center and back out again, it provided him with the perfect opportunity to reflect on how far, in just a few years, he and the hospital had come.

Still, he knew he had not reached the end of the journey.

Thoughts *from* Leland Kaiser

HOW TO BECOME A "SYSTEMS THINKER"

Mark Scott is clearly a systems thinker. A systems thinker sees the big picture and how all the smaller parts fit into it.

It takes a systems perspective to change healthcare, even at the local level. Healthcare is very complex and does not yield easily to any one-dimensional analysis.

Much like putting together a 500-piece jigsaw puzzle, Mark started with the edges and just kept putting pieces together until he had a coherent system.

Let me explain the concept of systems consciousness. The lowest common denominator of the universe is consciousness.

When everything is reduced to its most fundamental level, there is only consciousness. Consciousness is the bedrock of the universe. It is the basic building block. Space, time, energy and matter are forms taken by consciousness. Consciousness exists independent of a brain or nervous system. The brain does not produce consciousness. It acts as a valve and limits consciousness.

Consciousness is constrained by the vehicle it occupies. A human can participate in a more expanded realm of awareness than a plant, which in turn has a more inclusive consciousness than a rock. However, they are all conscious to varying degrees.

The only limitation you will ever face is the limitation of your own consciousness. All limitations, therefore, are self-imposed. Every apparent resource limitation is actually a consciousness limitation.

This means we are never limited by the universe, but only by our limited mental models of the universe. In many cases, people don't even realize they have mental models. They simply assume the only way to view a thing is the way they view it. Until you learn to doubt your mental models, there is no room for expanded learning.

The problem with contemporary healthcare is its collective mental model. It is a limited model and will not significantly improve the health and well-being of our population, regardless of how long and hard we try. We need a new mental model based on abundance, the pursuit of wellness, potentiation of people, community collaboration and the assumption of personal responsibility. Until we adopt such a model, things will get worse at the same time we are spending more and more trying to make things better.

A systems consciousness, which views everything as an individualized expression of the One, suggests a new mental model based on interdependence, resource sharing and information integration. The new mental model perceives the community as a living organism and views every organization in the community as an organ in that organism.

Resource sharing creates high levels of abundance not available in a highly competitive, materialistic mental model, such as the one currently in favor in American healthcare.

A unified mental model integrates allopathic, complementary and alternative care. It places the consumer in the center of the healthcare equation and uses the information technology of the Internet.

An individual gaining a systems awareness removes the lines of separation that have diminished his past work. A community with a systems awareness moves toward total systems integration of all health and human service agencies. Like a jigsaw puzzle, each piece is fitted to the other pieces. Most American communities do not have a resource problem. Instead, they have a consciousness problem that prevents them from sharing their abundance.

Never accept an unacceptable reality. Change it! Social and personal empowerment are the natural results of a systems consciousness. We are not victims. We are victors. We are limited only by the scope of our collective imagination.

Eventually, we will appoint people in our organizations to imagine a better future. This "dream team" will explore the limits of human imagination and intuition. The evolution of healthcare in our communities will greatly accelerate at this point of shared awareness. We will no longer be the victims of our past, with its centuries of blind groping and experimentation. We will be creators of our future.

Mark Scott did this at MCMC. You can do it in your organization and your community. Begin connecting people to meet and discuss their preferred future. Become a conscious systems builder.

CHAPTER 10

Bringing it All Together

Mark Scott never fooled himself for a minute into thinking that building a cancer center in The Dalles was the best business decision he'd ever made. No matter how he crunched the numbers, a cancer center wouldn't fly financially.

Scott believed the Mid-Columbia region simply wasn't populated enough to keep a cancer center busy enough to be financially independent. But he was determined to build one anyway and, once again, Mid-Columbia Medical Center board members showed their belief in him by throwing the full measure of their support behind his latest project. Their CEO had come to them frequently over the past several years with initiatives they never thought they'd be considering as hospital board members. But Scott hadn't let them down yet.

In fall 1999, MCMC's financial health was as robust as it ever had been. Scott had helped eliminate all of the hospital's debt and had built a healthy stockpile of reserves. In presenting his vision of a cancer center to board members, Scott was honest about its bleak financial forecast. Chances were it wouldn't turn a profit any time soon. Scott's best-case scenario showed the cancer center possibly showing a positive cash flow in three years. But MCMC board members were sold on their CEO's belief that it was simply the right thing to do.

Scott saw a new cancer center as MCMC's gift to a community that had supported its hospital so well since its inception.

While patients from the region were, at that time, able to receive chemotherapy at MCMC, those requiring radiation therapy had to make repeated three-hour round-trips to Portland. Scott felt it was unconscionable to continue sending patients away from their homes for care during the most trying time of their lives. For years, he had vowed to remedy the situation.

"I started thinking about building a cancer center right after we implemented Planetree," Scott said. "The results of every community-needs analysis we had done over the years showed that having access to cancer care locally was the number-one priority of area residents. This community had done a good job of building a support system for cancer patients that included volunteers who would drive people to Portland and back for the treatments. But the bottom line was that people had to make that trip every day for 30 to 40 consecutive days — and often through terrible weather. Cancer treatment is arduous enough without having to endure that."

When Scott began to consider a cancer center, he believed the prospects were especially bleak. Under normal circumstances, a cancer center in The Dalles could expect to draw patients from any community in the region not served by a closer facility. But through the 1990s, relations between MCMC and Hood River Memorial Hospital remained as frigid as the winter east wind that blew through the Columbia River Gorge. In developing a pro forma for a cancer center, Scott had to assume he could not count on many patients coming from the region's second-largest community — even though MCMC's center would be an hour closer than alternatives in Portland.

By 2001, though, the four hospitals serving the Mid-Columbia region (MCMC and Hood River Memorial in Oregon, and Skyline Hospital and Klickitat Valley Hospital in Goldendale and White Salmon, Washington, respectively) had forged an informal alliance, signaling a new era of cooperation.

Scott felt better about his odds of getting referrals from physicians in all of the communities surrounding The Dalles. Even so, he couldn't make the planned cancer center pencil-out financially.

"We looked at it 90 different ways," Scott said. "From a business perspective, it looked marginal from every angle."

But the human perspective was now driving the decision-making process at MCMC. The hospital had to remain profitable, of course, but it enjoyed financial stability that would allow MCMC to take on a potentially risky project, knowing it could be subsidized with income from other sources. Afforded the luxury of being able to assign financial performance a lower priority than community need, Scott knew his cancer center would be a no-brainer. Especially the kind of cancer center he had in mind.

In the new millennium, all MCMC activities were focused on the quest to meet one or more of the elements that comprised the organization's broader definition of health.

Signs of MCMC's commitment to caring not just for the biological needs of patients and families, but also their social, spiritual, intellectual and environmental needs could be seen and felt throughout the hospital — in the family-centered approach to care in the birthing center and medical-surgical units; Planetree's comprehensive educational component; the hospital's hotel-like accommodations and design features; the beautiful chapel, serene quiet spaces, meditative labyrinth and healing garden; the innovative Center for Mind and Body Medicine; the guest musicians; the artwork — everywhere.

Still, no single program brought all of the components together in a perfect manifestation of MCMC's quest to merge the science of medicine with the art of healing. Scott intended for MCMC's cancer center to be that program.

The new center would bring together the most advanced technology and treatments available with the package of complementary therapies MCMC had been employing through the Planetree conversion and mind-body center programs.

From the standpoint of technology and clinical expertise, Scott intended to make sure patients and their families could expect nothing less than they would find at the largest metropolitan cancer centers. And in addressing the spectrum of patient needs, he planned to create a center whose diverse array of healing tools would be unrivaled.

By this time, Scott and staff would not even consider any other approach to developing a new program. But even as he saw a new cancer center as a gift to his community, Scott, the CEO, also felt a facility this unique might draw patients from beyond the local service area. He still didn't hold out much hope that the cancer center would be a profit center soon, but every patient MCMC got that it didn't expect would help.

Scott had adamantly shot down a suggestion that MCMC conduct a community fund-raising campaign to support construction of the center.

"I was totally against that," he said. "I always wanted the center to be a gift to our community, and I had no intention of going out there with our hands out asking for money. The hospital was making money. People who worked there got paid a good wage. Doctors were doing well. I didn't want money going to us that could have been used to help address some of the many fundamental needs that were going unmet in our community."

The new cancer center would be constructed against a hill on the southeast edge of the MCMC campus, overlooking the beautiful labyrinth. Scott, of course, enlisted the services of an architect to help design the facility, but he and his team provided much of the general design direction.

"Given our experience with Planetree and the Center for Mind and Body Medicine, we knew how to do this," he said. "We had learned a great deal about form and function; intuitively, we knew what it had to look like. We just needed an architect to draw it for us."

What MCMC did not have was the expertise to run the medical component of the facility. With neither a medical nor radiation oncologist on staff, MCMC had only been able to offer chemotherapy services through a partnership with a visiting Portland medical group. Staffing a cancer center would require full-time oncology specialists.

Scott sent a request for proposals to Portland hospitals to explore a more formal and comprehensive cancer-care partnership. Predictably, at least to Scott, most of the hospitals thought they had a better idea.

"We were looking for a partner, but almost everybody we met tried to talk us out of building the center. They just wanted us to bundle up our patients and send them to Portland."

It wasn't until Scott met Norman Willis, M.D., that he heard the words he wanted to hear. Scott told Willis of his unique plans for the center and his intention of employing intensity-modulated radiation therapy (IMRT), the state-of-the-art technology he had learned about at a meeting of the Radiological Society of America. Willis, who was president of Radiation Oncologists and medical director of radiation oncology for Legacy Health System, a Portland-area hospital group, told Scott he was definitely interested in working with MCMC, on Scott's terms.

Willis would provide a medical director and medical physicist to establish and initially staff the radiation oncology department at MCMC's cancer center. In addition, medical oncologists would rotate once a week from Portland to The Dalles to oversee the chemotherapy program until MCMC was able to recruit its own full-time staff.

MCMC was ahead of even Legacy in making the investment in IMRT, but Willis's team was experienced in developing new radiation technologies. He also had a good source for potential candidates to direct Scott's new program.

After enjoying more than a decade of almost magical experiences in finding key personnel for his unique programs, Scott, in late 2000, had become a hard man to surprise. Still, even he could not believe his good fortune when Keith Stelzer showed up at his office to learn more about the unusual opportunity that a colleague had described to him.

If Scott could have designed the perfect physician to direct his new cancer center, even his imagination couldn't have come up with Stelzer. Sitting in front of him was one of the most qualified experts in state-of-the-art radiation technologies. Possessor of both an M.D., and Ph.D. A practitioner and researcher. A man of science who also was deeply spiritual.

Stelzer had heard about the MCMC opportunity in October 2000 when he was greeted by a phone call from a friend asking if he knew of any good candidates for an unusual practice opportunity. After spending three years as a resident and another seven as a faculty member at the University of Washington Medical School, Stelzer had helped train a lot of talented cancer specialists. Friends and colleagues routinely called asking for his recommendations.

But this call from his friend Tom Wynne, M.D., was different, and when Stelzer hung up the phone, he found himself thinking this might be the first time he would keep to himself the news of the unique opportunity he'd just learned about.

At the University of Washington, Stelzer was involved in leading-edge treatment and clinical research in radiation therapy. Only in his thirties, he already had become one of the world's preeminent experts in using highly conformed radiation treatments for brain tumors and had presented investigations into the new IMRT modality. IMRT allowed physicians to more precisely home in on cancer cells, sparing damage to surrounding cells and tissue. Stelzer's was one of very few cancer centers that had begun using the state-of-the-art radiation treatment technology.

Stelzer's background as a residency program director in radiation oncology at the University of Washington made him familiar with physicians trained in the latest radiation techniques.

That is why Wynne had called Stelzer. Wynne, who had finished the University of Washington residency program a year after Stelzer, was practicing in a Portland radiation oncology clinic. He explained to Stelzer that his clinic had been asked to provide consulting services and temporary staffing for a cancer center being built by a small hospital in the Columbia River Gorge.

Wynne asked his friend if he knew of a talented, young radiation oncologist interested in moving from bustling Seattle and a state-of-the-art university hospital to a quiet, rural town and a small, though uncommonly innovative, hospital.

Stelzer listened intently as Wynne described what had transpired at MCMC over the past decade, leading up to the planned construction of a unique cancer center. Wynne described the plans for the center, which would merge state-of-the-art technology, including IMRT, with a host of complementary therapies, from acupuncture to yoga.

That a small hospital 80 miles from Portland would be one of the first on the West Coast to employ IMRT was intriguing enough to Stelzer; no Portland hospital had even purchased the technology. But the whole-person concept that MCMC was trying to build around the technological component led Stelzer to hang up the phone convinced that the only person he'd talk to about the opportunity would be his wife, Susan.

He was surprised he was suddenly so open to the idea of leaving Seattle.

"I had a really good job," Stelzer said. "After I came out of my residency, I was given incredible opportunities at the University of Washington that helped me in ways that most physicians my age weren't able to benefit from."

Still, the demands of Stelzer's job were becoming increasingly at odds with his desire to have a quality family life with his wife and two children. As if teaching medical students, performing clinical research and actually treating patients weren't enough, Stelzer also was traveling more frequently. If he wasn't on a plane, chances were he was sitting in one of Seattle's notorious traffic jams, late again for dinner.

"More-and-more often, I was getting home after the kids had gone to bed," Stelzer said. "My career was going great, but I felt like I was missing out on some important things at home."

When Stelzer stepped into Scott's office for their first meeting, Scott wasn't sure what he had done to deserve this long string of good fortune that kept delivering the right person at the right time. But he wasn't about to question it. He just started talking, as enthusiastically and convincingly as ever, about his plans for a one-of-a-kind cancer-care center. The more Stelzer heard, the better it sounded.

"Mark told me about the history of Planetree, and I thought that was fascinating and very unique," Stelzer said. "They were just breaking ground on the cancer center, so we took a walk to the site and Mark discussed his vision. He talked about his goal of raising the bar in cancer care by combining the latest technology with an approach to care that really involved the patient and family, and addressed the spectrum of their needs. Mark described a vision I had never seen or heard of in practice."

The idea of being in on the ground floor of such a unique cancer center intrigued Stelzer, and his initial impression of The Dalles was positive. But with Stelzer already having a great job and established life in Seattle, Scott figured that it would take a lot more to lure this perfect candidate away. He was wrong.

"It was a very obvious decision for me," Stelzer said. "And I made it before I got back home to Seattle. Somewhere between Vancouver and Centralia, it became very clear to me that this was the right thing to do, and I didn't have any hesitation taking the job."

MCMC's new cancer facility was completed in February 2001. It was, as Scott promised, one-of-a-kind. Before patients or visitors would enter or begin treatment, they could see this was no ordinary cancer center. Even at 21,000 square feet, with a facade of stucco and glass, the building blended almost naturally with the surroundings — the steep hillside behind it and the terrazzo stone labyrinth and beautiful gardens in front of it.

Approaching the building, a visitor or patient could see no signs that it was a cancer center — just a small sign in gold letters above the entrance that read "Celilo" and the peaceful sound of water tumbling over rocks.

Scott had agonized over a name for his center, repeatedly sending his marketing consultant back to the drawing board because he had yet to be inspired by any of the dozens of names offered for his consideration. Scott spent scant seconds pondering each suggested name placed before him. A cancer center this unique had to have a meaningful name. It was out there, somewhere, and Scott knew he would recognize it instantly when he read it.

"I knew we didn't want to name it after someone who had lost their fight with cancer, and I sure as hell didn't want a cutesy name," Scott said. "I think I must have been presented with 300 ideas that didn't work."

Scott was beginning to feel like an expectant parent, on the verge of the due date and still without a name for his child. Finally, the equally exasperated consultant slid one more piece of paper in front of him containing the simple, six-letter word "Celilo."

"I knew instantly that Celilo was perfect," Scott said. "I knew in my soul that's what the name should be."

Celilo was borrowed from the rich Native American history of the Mid-Columbia region. Before they disappeared with the construction of The Dalles Dam in 1957, the spectacular, crescent-shaped Celilo Falls represented one of the most important fisheries on the Columbia River. For thousands of years of human civilization, it was one of history's great marketplaces.

In *Recalling Celilo*, author Elizabeth Woody wrote, "So abundant were the fish passing Celilo on their upriver journey that the fish caught there could feed a whole family through the winter. No one would starve if they could work. Even those incapable of physical work could share other talents... It was a dignified existence. Peaceful, perhaps due in part to the sound of the water that echoes in people's minds and the negative ions produced by the falls. Research has shown this to generate a feeling of well-being in human beings."

The word "celilo" (or "wyam" in several Native American languages) means "echo of falling water" or "sound of water upon the rocks," and water was one of the key environmental elements of the new cancer center. A beautiful water feature was built at the base of the building's strikingly curved, two-story reflective glass foyer. Water tumbled over rocks adorned with a series of Native American petroglyphs, including one called "The Medicine Man."

The rich history, the connection with healing and sharing, all gave the name Celilo the same sense of sacredness that Scott envisioned in the cancer center. There could be no other name; still, Scott first met with representatives of the region's Warm Springs Tribe to receive their blessing of his plans before he made the name official. Local tribal members so approved of the name being affiliated with the center that they later agreed to participate in Celilo's dedication ceremony.

The environment of Celilo was an unexpected surprise to those who entered, but especially those who had experiences at other cancer centers. This included, of course, professionals like Stelzer, who understood soon after Celilo opened the advantages of treating patients in a beautiful setting that offered such a vast array of healing tools.

"You realized suddenly how much more challenging it had been to take care of your patients in the typical cold, sterile, cancer center environment," Stelzer said. "You were usually dealing with an outside factor that affected your patient and their receptiveness to you."

Stelzer said that, in retrospect, his patients always seemed to be upset or frustrated by something — the way they were treated by staff or the cold atmosphere of the center.

"As a physician, you have difficulty connecting with your patient because he or she sees you as part of that problem, so a wall comes up," he said. "It's even more difficult to get important concepts across to patients or educate them about their disease and encourage them to take some control themselves."

Stelzer discovered early on that the environment of Celilo presented no such challenges. The contrast between the mindset of his patients in this new setting and those in his former practice was striking but not difficult to understand.

"When you are just diagnosed with cancer, your life has been turned upside down," Stelzer said. "It's important for you to understand your treatment options and learn how you can best fight your disease, but, of course, you're extremely anxious. That's not a mindset that's very conducive to learning."

Stelzer said patients who entered Celilo were, of course, still anxious, but they would also be thinking, "Wow, this isn't what I expected." At Celilo, patients were always greeted by a friendly and helpful receptionist at the front desk. Everyone else they met was extremely competent, very warm and very caring.

"So they'd start to feel more at ease," Stelzer said. "Then they'd have a seat in a comfortable chair in a waiting room that looks like a living room, and they'd start getting a massage right there. Then they'd be led back to the exam room, where I or my nurse would greet them. You could feel that a lot of the obstacles had been broken down before you even started talking with them."

When he walked into the room and met these newly diagnosed people and their families for the first time, it was obvious that they were in a different state of mind than his former patients, Stelzer said.

"I knew I had a better chance of reaching my patients than in any other environment I'd been in," he said.

As patient-care coordinator, Lyn Vincenzo, R.N., served as Celilo's unofficial host and central resource person. She personally met with each patient and family member and provided a tour of the building and an introduction to the center's programs and amenities.

Vincenzo's goal was to get to know the patients and to find out as soon as possible what their mindset was, to determine any specific needs they had and to help demystify the process of receiving treatment.

"Generally speaking, cancer patients are very frightened, so you want to do everything you can to decrease their fear and give them back as much control of their lives as possible," she said.

Planetree had taught the MCMC staff that education and information were key to helping put patients in control of their disease and its care. At Celilo, a small resource library was one of the first things patients saw when they entered, and it was the first stop on Vincenzo's tour.

Patients would then learn about the array of complementary tools that comprised Celilo's unique Integrated Therapy Program, which borrowed from and expanded on the offerings of MCMC's Center for Mind and Body Medicine. During the course of their care, Celilo patients, as well as family members, were encouraged to participate in any or all of these offerings.

In the conservative community of The Dalles, some patients elected to take a more traditional approach to cancer care. But even in Celilo's earliest days, it was not unusual to see an elderly farmer in bib overalls receiving a massage in the lobby.

If they wished, patients could even have a massage during their chemotherapy treatment. "You could just see the stress drain from their faces," Vincenzo said.

The array of stress reduction and relaxation offerings that were part of Celilo's Integrated Therapy Program included tai chi, yoga, journal writing classes, rhythmic drumming and guided relaxation sessions, which had been shown to reduce anxiety and insomnia. Aromatherapy and music therapy were incorporated into many of these offerings.

One of the most unusual, and most frequently used, features of Celilo was a spa and meditation facility called the Center for Mindfulness. In this setting, patients and family members could have a massage, soak in a Jacuzzi or enjoy the sauna. A beautiful meditative room, looking out on a healing garden, offered a place for quiet reflection.

Acupuncture was incorporated into the care of patients as part of Celilo's Traditional Chinese Medicine Program. In addition to acupuncture, the program offered herbal and nutritional therapy that was used at Celilo to strengthen the immune system, improve organ function and reduce the pain, nausea and fatigue often associated with cancer and its treatment.

On Celilo's second floor, the chemotherapy area offered either private rooms with sweeping views of the Columbia River or a group setting where patients could socialize, watch movies, listen to music or just enjoy the view out onto the hillside. It was not uncommon to walk into Celilo and hear a noise few would expect in a cancer treatment center — laughter.

"From the start, the environment of Celilo clearly encouraged patients to be supportive of each other," Vincenzo said. "It was amazing to see how helpful it was for patients just to talk to someone else about their fears and what they were going through. Celilo provided the atmosphere where people felt safe to do that."

Scott considered Celilo hallowed ground, and after the grand opening events that afforded the public the chance to see MCMC's gift to the community, he worked hard to keep the facility as serene as possible. No overhead pages echoed through the halls, and hospital staff were discouraged from wandering around the building without a specific purpose.

"From the start, Celilo felt like a magical place, and we didn't want the normal, day-to-day activities that occur in the hospital to alter that," Scott said. "Yes, there were conference rooms in the building, but they were to be used for patients or after hours. I didn't want patients, in their most trying times, to have their thoughts interrupted by a page for John Doe or by lousy Muzak."

Scott said Celilo was sacred ground not just for patients, but for MCMC's staff, too.

"They needed to have an environment conducive to helping them be all they needed to be for their patients," he explained.

Keith Stelzer needed a while to get used to practicing in a cancer-care setting as different as Celilo. Perhaps the biggest hurdle was getting out of the mindset of just presenting the risks and benefits of treatment and then talking about informed consent and the other rote information that he'd been going over for years.

"It took some time for it to really sink in that now I had so much more to offer my patients," Stelzer said. "As a physician, you are limited in what you can do to attack cancer and treat your patients. It felt liberating to have access to this new world of tools that I could offer patients to help address their symptoms and other aspects of dealing with this terrible disease and getting through some rough treatments."

Celilo may have been MCMC's gift back to its community, but before long, word about the new cancer-care center was reaching out-of-towners. Celilo's early patient volume was significantly ahead of Scott's forecasts, and he knew the local cancer incidence rates didn't increase just because there was now a local resource for treatment.

With the only IMRT program in the vicinity, Scott suspected Celilo might benefit from some Portland referrals, at least until Portland hospitals installed the technology. But, as Scott scanned his patient origin studies, he saw patients coming from many unsuspected places. Hood River referrals were stronger than he had anticipated; patients also were coming from Bend, two hours south, and other communities in central Oregon. There were even patients from southern Oregon — people who were traveling as far as 300 miles to receive care at Celilo, passing right through Portland on the way.

In its first year, Celilo attracted patients from seven states. In future years, patients from 28 states would make the trip. Many were coming for state-of-the-art radiation treatment that was only available in a few centers west of the Mississippi. Others had heard about Celilo's efforts to integrate body, mind and spirit in the care process.

Whatever brought them, their presence was proving Scott wrong. Celilo, MCMC's gift to the community and Scott's monument to the perfectly pure patient-care environment, would be profitable by the end of its first year.

Thoughts *from* Leland Kaiser

HOW TO CREATE A
POWERFUL HEALING ENVIRONMENT

It happened at Celilo. Spirituality and science came together to create an integrated approach to cancer care. As a result, Celilo is now a destination cancer treatment center. Patients arrive from long distances to seek care. Visiting hospital teams come to learn how to provide this kind of whole-person care, where body and spirit are both nourished in an environment of love and healing.

Celilo appears to grow up from the ground. It rises almost as a natural feature of the land. This is part of the sacred commitment to healing architecture that is Celilo. Years ago, Native American medicine men did their healing work here. Now, this sacred site is occupied by the latest technological approaches to cancer care. But the traditions of previous indigenous healers have been retained.

Every building used for healthcare makes an architectural statement. Celilo is no exception. Celilo talks about unity of spirit, mind and body. It views cancer as an opportunity for spiritual growth. A cure for the disease is always sought. If this is not possible, healing is attempted. The goal is to heal every patient and cure all those who can be cured.

The labyrinth outside Celilo is a loving reminder to patients and family members alike that life is a journey, and for some people, cancer is part of that life journey. The labyrinth helps walkers better navigate the ups and downs, and twists and turns of their lives. It is a powerful metaphor for the healing journey. Rather than being a victim, the walker becomes the hero on a heroic journey. Rather than just a recipient of care, the patient becomes a full participant in his own recovery.

Celilo is ahead of its time. It is now where many cancer treatment centers will eventually be in the future. Cancer treatment should always take place within a spiritual context, since cancer for many patients is a wake-up call that awakens their spirituality. For these patients, their disease is also an ally that enables them to refocus their attention from the mundane details of daily life to the purpose for their existence on this planet.

If a cancer treatment center does not have a sacred dimension, how can it help patients view their disease as an avenue for personal transformation? Celilo does precisely this. It is a beautiful demonstration of the redeeming, regenerating properties of a dreaded disease. It offers its patients hope and light. It takes patients places that most cancer centers do not even know exist. It offers hope, rather than fearful resignation. It offers love in addition to clinical objectivity. And every now and then, it even generates a miracle in terms of a patient's total recovery.

Staff members at Celilo are chosen as much for their advanced qualities of consciousness as for their technical competence. A great head and an open, loving heart are valued equally in the recruitment process.

In my opinion, of all of Mark Scott's accomplishments, Celilo best reflects his own revolution in spiritual consciousness. He reached toward greater integration of spirit and body. He achieved that integration, just as Celilo has achieved it.

Most cancer facilities I visit underwhelm me, rather than overwhelm me. Many are simply buildings that contain equipment and provide jobs for associated personnel. These facilities look, feel and smell like sick places. Most are rather drab and austere. By contrast, Celilo overwhelmed me. I knew during my first visit that this was indeed a magical place. It was doing what many other centers would only learn to do in the future.

Celilo was providing an exciting new paradigm for cancer care — a paradigm that was both scientific and spiritual, that both cured and healed. It was patient- and family-centered. It was community-oriented. It provided many people with hope and a pathway through a dreaded disease.

At Celilo, the patient was family. The patient was loved and nourished. This was such a different approach to care. I did not see it in large medical centers. How did it happen at this little-known place in rural Oregon? The answer was simple: The right people came together at the right time in the right way to create it. The inspired leadership of Mark Scott was there. His inspired leadership attracted many health professionals from near and far. Here was their chance to make a breakthrough. They knew that opportunities like that seldom came in the lifetime of any health professional. Conditions were right. They responded to the call. Celilo happened!

The good news is that Celilo can be replicated by any group of dedicated health professionals that recognizes both the spiritual and scientific dimensions of disease and the power of a healing environment. It is a working model ready for export and adaptation in many different environments. I am grateful I witnessed its birth. I will be even more grateful to witness its progeny.

CHAPTER 11

STORYTELLING AND CELEBRATION

Celebration and storytelling had become an important tradition at Mid-Columbia Medical Center by the time the Celilo Cancer Center opened in 2001. Their origins went back to the first curriculum for MCMC University, the theatrical setting through which hospital staff passed to learn their important role in personalizing, humanizing and demystifying the hospital experience.

"A great deal of what we taught in the university was through stories," Scott said. "And it just expanded from there."

Soon after developing the university training concept, Scott read about a CEO who started each of his board meetings with an inspirational story. Scott quickly added a storytelling component to his department manager meetings. Each week, a manager shared a story about a patient's positive experience at the hospital or an employee's special efforts to improve a patient's or visitor's experience — anything that would inspire others or depict MCMC's values in action.

"I thought storytelling was a great way to extend our culture deeper into the organization," Scott said. "It felt like one more good way to get everybody to understand what our core values were and get them all on the same page."

From the department manager meetings, Scott expanded his storytelling requirement to interdepartmental meetings. He reinforced the importance of the activity by requiring department managers to forward to him the minutes of each meeting.

"I didn't really care what was on the agenda specifically, but I wanted to learn from the stories employees were telling," Scott said. "I felt if people were always talking about our values and sharing examples of how they were playing out on a daily basis, they'd remain inspired by them and committed to them. And I also thought that, in the process of telling inspirational stories, they would start seeing a transition from their work being just a job to being something they love."

Of all his accomplishments as a hospital CEO, Scott believed turning MCMC employees into storytellers was among his most successful. "I think storytelling is a magical management act," he said.

Over the years as CEO, Scott developed a flair for the theatrical. Like storytelling, Scott used celebrations and ceremonies to help impart the values of the organization. Department directors never knew what, or what character, to expect at meetings, retreats and parties. One would feature Scott and his senior managers dressed in tuxedoes, acting as servants to their employees; another would have Scott appearing as William Wallace, hero of *Braveheart*, thrusting a massive sword into a stage and orating on the virtues of being a free, independent healthcare organization, unencumbered by the restraints of a large, regional or national system.

After the opening of Celilo, Scott held a special dedication celebration with department managers. During the event, he sat near Celilo's waterfall feature. Beautiful harp music could be heard above the sounds of the water falling over rocks.

Scott recently had expanded his spirituality initiative by adding music thanatologist Anna Fiasca to the MCMC staff. A longtime resident of the area, Fiasca had discovered the Chalice of Repose Project, a graduate-level school of music thanatology housed within St. Patrick Hospital in Missoula, Montana. Music thanatology is akin to music therapy, but it differs in its intention, which is to address the complex needs of dying patients.

Scott paid for Fiasca's two-year thanatology training and then brought her back to MCMC to conduct deathbed vigils for hospitalized patients. During a vigil, Fiasca, who had formerly played in orchestras and ensembles, would join the patient and family members, singing and playing harp. Her thanatology training taught her to notice changes in the patient's breathing and heart rate, and to change her music in response to body rhythms.

Family members universally praised the thanatology program, and Scott began relying on Fiasca's musical skills in other settings as well.

For the grand opening of Celilo, Scott had positioned Fiasca on the labyrinth in front of the cancer center. Scott's managers had been led from the medical office building to Celilo and, as each filed past him, Scott presented him or her with a Native American medicine bag with healing artifacts from the Confederated Tribes of the Warm Springs Reservation. He had a personal message for each manager, expressing what he or she had meant to MCMC and to him.

By now, Scott knew that he would soon be leaving MCMC, but he had not yet announced his departure.

After the grand opening ceremony, the MCMC managers gathered on the labyrinth and listened to a member of the Warm Springs tribe tell a story about nature and healing. Later, they participated in a traditional smudging ceremony. Smudging, the burning of bundled herbs (in this case, sage) called smudge sticks, is a rite of purification in many Native American traditions.

Mark Scott retired as CEO of MCMC in the spring of 2002, but evidence of his influence as an innovator and inspirational leader remains throughout the hospital.

In fact, Scott helped assure that the organization he had taken so far over 20-plus years maintained its commitment to continuous improvement of the hospital experience for patients and visitors by hand-picking and garnering board support for his successor.

When Duane Francis was promoted to assume the reins of MCMC in 2002, it brought to fruition the succession strategy Scott had put into place six years earlier. Francis had first joined MCMC in 1984, recruited away from Utah Valley Regional Medical Center in Provo by then-CEO Gary Rood. The Bountiful, Utah, native became MCMC's controller only three years after graduating from Brigham Young University. In another three years, with Scott leading MCMC, Francis was promoted to chief financial officer.

As much as Francis loved working for Scott and believed in the direction in which he was taking MCMC, his goal had always been to run his own hospital. In 1991, with the Planetree implementation in full swing and Scott reenergized as a leader, Francis knew that opportunity would not come soon at MCMC. He left MCMC for a job that seemingly offered a better chance to reach his goal sooner.

Mercy Medical Center, located in the southern Oregon community of Roseburg, had been led by a Sister of Mercy, Jacquetta Taylor, for nearly three decades. With her retirement nearing, the Mercy board was beginning to plan for her succession. Francis was hired as vice president of finance with the promise that he would be seriously considered as Taylor's replacement.

Throughout Francis' stay at Mercy, the hospital was embroiled in a fiercely competitive battle with a for-profit hospital across town. With a population of only 20,000 in Roseburg and a service area of approximately 65,000 people, the region wasn't large enough to support two hospitals. Though Mercy enjoyed the lion's share of the market, the emergence of managed care in the mid-1990s threatened to limit patients' choice of which hospital they could use. Concerned they might lose their market advantage despite being the community's preferred hospital, the Mercy board engaged outside consultants to help plan strategies for continued financial health in what was promising to be a predominantly managed care environment.

With no experience in the managed care arena, Mercy could benefit from an infusion of new ideas, Taylor thought. In 1996, she announced her retirement after 27 years of leading the organization. With so much at stake and a group of out-of-town consultants now calling many of the organization's shots, Francis concluded that the board would be looking outside of Mercy for its next leader.

So when Scott, on his way home from a three-month sabbatical on his Harley Davidson, stopped by Roseburg with a job offer for his old friend, Francis was all ears. Scott wanted Francis to return to MCMC. He offered a senior vice president position and as much of a promise as he could give that Francis was next in line for CEO.

Seeing his opportunity pass in Roseburg, and knowing Scott was in the planning stages for his own retirement, Francis returned to MCMC.

For the next six years, he worked closely with his mentor on a wide range of major initiatives, including the development of the hospital's own insurance product, Healthscape. When Scott announced his retirement, MCMC's board of trustees gave Francis the opportunity he had been seeking.

After spending his entire professional career in healthcare, Francis had his own ideas about how to run a hospital. His style of leadership was in many ways the virtual opposite of Scott's. But in the most important matter — maintaining MCMC's commitment to its broader definition of health, its core values and continuous improvement of the hospital experience for patients and families — the two men's philosophies were completely aligned.

And, of course, it would have been impossible to work that closely for that long with any mentor and not be considerably influenced. Under Francis's leadership, storytelling and celebration maintained their prominent status in the MCMC culture. His formal dedication of Celilo near Christmas in 2005 — a "thank you" to the local tribe that had allowed MCMC to borrow its name for the cancer center — was very much inspired by Scott.

Francis invited Charles Littleleaf, a shaman from the Confederated Tribes of the Warm Springs Reservation, to officially dedicate Celilo three years after it had opened with a prayer and smudging ceremony.

Littleleaf offered a gift to Celilo of a flute, handcarved from a fallen walnut tree under which an elder named Sally Ike used to advise tribal members. Francis was taken by the similarities between, and symbolism of, Ike and the walnut tree and Hippocrates and the planetree under which he taught medical students, which had inspired MCMC's development over the previous 15 years.

The flute, as well as a quilt made by Ike, are now stored in a display case inside the Celilo foyer.

Francis has taken the tradition of celebration and storytelling in new directions. For example, MCMC's Shades of Planetree program is Francis' take on a traditional manager and employee recognition program. Employees nominate coworkers for recognition by sharing their stories of MCMC's values in action. Those recognized each month are given a pewter pen (reinforcing the storytelling theme). A formal annual celebration honors all monthly nominees and the year's best stories. Francis even involves the MCMC board, enlisting the directors' help in choosing the best stories from the group of nominees. The walls of MCMC's hallways feature framed photos of the Shades of Planetree winners and their stories, again reinforcing to employees and guests alike the importance of service and honoring the storytelling tradition at MCMC.

Thoughts *from* Leland Kaiser

THE IMPORTANCE OF RITES, RITUALS AND CELEBRATIONS

An exceptional CEO is no stranger to rite, ritual and celebration. He knows ceremonies of the human spirit are important to maintain vision, purpose and morale in the organization. A healthcare organization has a mythic dimension. The mythic dimension is also the spiritual dimension. Accessing spirit is beyond mind, and this is precisely where rite, ritual and celebration reside.

An inspiring orientation for new employees is a good example of an important rite. During orientation, a foundation is laid for the new employee, and he or she is welcomed into a new social unit. This goes far beyond the reach of the conscious mind. It taps into the unconscious and archetypal levels. Here the Hero, Savior, Mother, Trickster and Mentor archetypes stand ready for evocation.

If done properly, orientation aligns the spiritual purpose of the organization with the spiritual purpose of the employee. Doing one means accomplishing the other. The job is then more than a job. It is an important step in the eternal journey of unfoldment.

Promotion is an important ritual for all employees. It is something the whole organization should be involved in. It is a special recognition of individual and organizational accomplishment.

We can learn something from the secret lodges in this respect. Lodge members take various initiations as they progress in the lodge. These are always ceremonies of great pomp and circumstance. They are outer recognitions of inner accomplishments. Of course, promotion should always be given on the basis of real accomplishments known and recognized by the entire organization.

Each time the organization reaches a milestone in its evolution, celebrations are in order. Fun, mirth, humor and good times nourish the human spirit. We love to attend a great party or victory celebration. This should not be as routine as the annual Christmas party or company picnic.

Eventually, we will return to our ancient heritage and have celebrations more in tune with the cycles of nature. The whole universe runs in cycles, and so should we. Therefore, there are two types of celebrations: One celebrates the seasons and the other celebrates important milestones in the evolution of the organization. The organization's birthday might be one of these, where we gather to honor our founders and reaffirm our loyalty to their visions and aspirations. Mark Scott was known for the creative, extravagant and sometimes outrageous ceremonies he designed to honor his employees.

He realized that as the healthcare marketplace becomes more brutal, the importance of rite, ritual and celebration increases. Something eternal must guide our way through the thicket of present difficulties. We must have something more to live for than short-term survival.

In the next few years, the CEO must fulfill the important role of mythmaker. Mark was successful because he changed the collective mindset of his organization. He helped his associates think in new and expanded ways. As a result, he created a new reality at MCMC.

CHAPTER 12

AN ENDURING LEGACY

Mark Scott's good fortune is referred to often in the preceding chapters, and indeed, every time he needed a champion to help ensure a program's success, someone stepped forward — seemingly, on more than one occasion, by some kind of divine intervention.

In fact, the transformation of Mid-Columbia Medical Center would not have been possible, had the organization not been unusually blessed with a large core of individuals — doctors, nurses, managers, other employees, volunteers and board members — who were exceptional at their jobs, truly cared about people and were willing to embrace and facilitate fundamental and dramatic change.

Good people attract other good people, which is the principal reason MCMC has been able to maintain its standing as a hospital innovator for so many years.

A good example is Paul Cardosi, M.D., who became medical director of MCMC's Sleep Center in 2002. When Cardosi first visited MCMC in 1996, he couldn't comprehend what he was seeing and feeling. He was just wrapping up his residency at Oregon Health & Science University in Portland (OHSU), and since entering medical school, he had been able to visualize his idea of the perfect practice environment. But to now find himself seemingly surrounded by it, in this small hospital in this conservative rural community? Something had to be wrong.

A native of the East Coast, Cardosi had gravitated toward small, intimate settings for his schooling — Bucknell University for his undergraduate work and Dartmouth College for medical school. Now he was hoping to find a practice opportunity engaging enough to allow him to stay in Oregon, a part of the country he had grown to love.

Like many of the transplants who have settled in the Columbia River Gorge, Cardosi was originally drawn by the world-class windsurfing. He'd learned the sport on a lake in New Hampshire and was so smitten with it that, when it was time for his residency training, he chose OHSU just to be near the fabled Gorge.

To stay in the area after his medical training was complete, Cardosi would have been willing to settle for less than his ideal job. In fact, he expected to. But as he walked through MCMC on his first visit, with two of Mark Scott's best spokespeople — Randy Carter and Joyce Powell-Morin — as tour guides, Cardosi could quickly feel the difference between this hospital and the many others he had experienced.

"The sense of caring and compassion that was held by doctors and nurses and everyone else was very evident," he remembered. "It was obvious that, to practice in this setting, you didn't just have to be a good, smart doctor, you really had to have the kind of personality that meshed with a very unique culture."

During residency training, Cardosi and other young physicians had been repeatedly upbraided by a particularly hard-nosed surgeon, and the experience left an indelible mark.

"We all had the attitude, 'Well, he's a good teacher, and he cares enough about us to degrade us,'" Cardosi remembered. "But I was never really convinced that this kind of behavior should have to be tolerated. I wanted to get away from that kind of environment as soon as possible."

At MCMC, it was obvious to Cardosi that physicians were expected to hang their egos on their office walls next to their degrees and to leave them there permanently.

"The people at MCMC didn't downplay the importance of technical proficiency, but proficiency in the human aspects of care were equally important," Cardosi said.

After visiting MCMC, the new physician and his wife, Mimi, an obstetrician/gynecologist, signed on without visiting another hospital.

Cardosi practiced internal medicine at MCMC initially. As his first Christmas holiday at MCMC approached, he prepared to spend most of his free time on call, answering calls from patients or making hospital rounds.

"Being the new guy, it was only natural that I would expect to get the least desirable call rotations," Cardosi said.

Instead, Cardosi was told he'd be able to enjoy some worry-free time off.

"I couldn't believe it when a colleague told me, 'You're not going to be on call Christmas or any of the holidays your first year. It's hard enough getting your practice started without that.' I had this overwhelming feeling of being supported by everybody."

Cardosi's story is typical of many individuals who have joined the MCMC family in the years since the Planetree implementation spurred the development of a unique healthcare setting. Even now, years after Scott's departure from the hospital, these special people continue to keep his vision of patient-centered care alive and well at MCMC.

Among this group is Michele Spatz, who, along with her longtime staff member Linda Stahl, has worked continuously to develop and enhance connections with the surrounding community.

In the Planetree Health Resource Center's early months, Spatz made the tour of local service clubs, introducing community members to the concept of the library and the information packets.

"I'd pass a couple examples of the packets around the room while I was talking," Spatz said. "Invariably, people would come up after my presentation and ask if they could keep one of the packets because they knew someone who had that diagnosis and they wanted to share the information. That's when I knew we were going to be successful."

While the Internet has dramatically improved laypeople's access to vast health information resources, Spatz and her staff remain as busy as ever helping patients and community members use knowledge to take a more active role in their own health maintenance.

A lecture series that Spatz launched in fall 1992 remains popular. The series frequently drew standing-room-only crowds in the Health Resource Center's 40-seat conference room, so it has been moved to the hospital campus to accommodate more attendees.

Resource Center staff also work closely with the local high school on an array of projects and are involved in health occupation classes at Columbia Gorge Community College in The Dalles.

"We think it's really important to work with young students because they are our future healthcare consumers," Spatz said. "Teaching them how to find reliable information gives them a skill they can use in their own self-care."

The Health Resource Center now features a cybercafé, with four personal computers offering free access to the Internet and interactive CD-ROM programs. Spatz also helped develop a comprehensive website (www.mcmc.net/library) offering online visitors information on area support groups, educational programs, an electronic library of searchable health articles and an online card catalog enabling users to search and request library resources.

The comprehensive information packets that were a critical component of MCMC's Planetree conversion remain a popular feature with patients and families. Initially implemented just for hospital inpatients, the service has been expanded to other clinical areas within the hospital, including visiting home-health services, same-day surgery, Celilo Cancer Center and MCMC's affiliated primary-care group. The latter was added after a physician complained to Spatz that the provider group "felt like a Third World country" because it wasn't offering information packets to its patients.

Clinic physicians and other health professionals now use prescription pads to request that information be compiled for their patients. In addition, the hospital's electronic medical record system was enhanced to give professionals the ability to request a patient information packet.

As a result of all these efforts, Spatz has developed a national reputation for expertise in the delivery of consumer health information. The Planetree library model is considered the gold standard, which many other organizations have tried to replicate. Spatz serves on regional and national committees addressing issues ranging from health literacy to accreditation of national health websites. She also teaches two accredited continuing-education classes on consumer health information for the Medical Library Association.

As impressive as her resume is, Spatz is just one of the many people who continue to make MCMC a unique healthcare institution.

Tia Bailey and Roberta Carson, who both remain in nursing positions with the hospital, and Joyce Powell-Morin and Dianne Storby, both now MCMC vice presidents, have collected stories over the years that illustrate the spirit of the people who have been part of MCMC's evolution from traditional hospital to Planetree experiment to comprehensive center for whole-person healing. Here are a few of those stories.

Storby remembered a phone call from an 89-year-old lady. The woman started by saying, "You know, I don't complain much and I love your hospital, but I want you to know that the last time I came, it wasn't quite as nice as it usually is." When Storby asked what was wrong, the woman explained that her roommate had kept the window curtains pulled shut, preventing her from seeing the beautiful view outside. The caller then told Storby, "But I want you to know that I'm not really complaining, because one day a woman came outside my door and played the harp (MCMC's music thanatologist Anna Fiasca), and she was just an angel."

Storby said Fiasca's presence provides a boost, not only for the patients, but for the staff as well. "It's happened to me several times," she said. "I'll be having a bad day, and then I'll walk around the corner and hear this beautiful harp music. It just changes my whole mood."

During the early days of the Planetree conversion, Joyce Powell-Morin said, she realized that the soaring MCMC atrium had become not just a focal point for the hospital building, but also a kind of town square where patients, medical staff and people from the larger community would gather.

"[The first time I realized it was] when the UPS driver felt comfortable enough to sit down at the piano and play a quick song after making a delivery," she said.

"And there were several occasions when Sue Kelly (a former MCMC nurse and accomplished pianist) would wheel patients down to the atrium and stand behind them and help them play," Powell-Morin continued. "It always meant so much to those patients."

Today, the hospital has added the requisite espresso cart to the atrium, helping to ensure it retains its communal nature.

Among the myriad stories of MCMC staff members who epitomize Planetree's patient-first philosophy, there is the story of a nurse named Julie. Storby explained that a cancer patient at the Celilo Cancer Center developed bronchial spasms before every chemotherapy session. This would delay the start of her treatment, often for several hours, and would throw off the center's schedule for the rest of the day.

"We'd have to slow everything way down until she calmed down enough to start treatment," Storby said.

Finally, the patient was introduced to Julie, who also was a licensed massage therapist. Julie had been coming to Celilo from Portland once a week to practice her massage skills, which she had been discouraged from using while nursing in Portland. Once Julie started working on the patient, other nurses were able to insert the IV and complete her treatment without her even noticing. It wasn't until the nurses were removing the IV that the woman noticed and tried to stop them because she thought she hadn't had her chemo yet.

"That's a good story from a patient perspective, but, if you look at it from a cold dollars-and-cents standpoint, it makes a hospital CEO feel really good," Storby said. "I think we were paying the nurse-massage therapist $17 an hour to perform a function that may have saved the hospital a thousand dollars in lost chemotherapy revenue because every-thing remained on schedule."

Roberta Carson remembered the way her staff responded to a Native American family whose loved one died at MCMC. As the nurses set about preparing to remove the body from the room, a family member said, "You can't move him yet; if you do, his spirit will wander forever." Although keeping the body of a deceased patient in a hospital room for several hours is difficult, the staff did not hesitate to make it happen.

"We did that out of respect for this family's beliefs," Carson said. "It was a little inconvenient for the staff, but it meant a lot to the family, and we had all relearned our priorities fairly quickly. That's the way we thought it should have been all along; but until [Planetree], we hadn't been encouraged to act that way."

Ever since the introduction of Planetree, MCMC has continued to roll out innovative programs designed to improve the hospital experience.

One of these offers patients the opportunity to receive a therapeutic visit from a pet, usually a dog. At its peak, the program was "staffed" by 19 animals, whose photographs often wound up occupying space on patient bookshelves, next to their children and grandchildren. One of the most popular pets was Scott's beloved black Lab, Bo.

Scott recalled hearing the story of one particularly belligerent patient who had been hurling obscenities at any nurse who neared his room. Finally, one nurse got up the nerve to ask the patient if he would be interested in a visit from one of the hospital's therapy pets.

"The patient's attitude changed immediately," Scott said. "He called Bo up onto his bed and threw an arm around him, and then took him for a walk down the hallway. After that, the patient was perfectly fine."

Even today, Tia Bailey continues to marvel at how different her working environment is from any other nurse she knows.

"It's not at all unusual for me to walk from the medical office building to the hospital and hear someone playing guitar or piano in the atrium, take an elevator ride with a friendly dog or hear the sounds of harp music in the halls of the patient wings," she said. "Of course, there's beautiful art on the walls, and I'm often 'tortured' by the smell of freshly baked cookies. It's a lot different from the days of dodging wheelchairs."

Other people charged with maintaining MCMC's caring legacy couldn't agree more. In fact, Keith Stelzer, Celilo's medical director of radiation oncology, believes that environment is so critical to a person's state of mind — whether a patient, family member or employee — that he takes a short, scenic walk from the parking lot to his office every morning.

"When I go into work every morning, I still get the same feeling that our patients do the first time they see Celilo," he said. "Unless it's pouring rain, I make sure I walk around to the front of the building, where the waterfall is, and that puts my mind in the right place to start the day."

Stelzer contrasted his daily experience with that of many health professionals who start their day by pulling into a huge parking lot, fighting their way across two streets and heading to the basement of a mega-health center.

"[The environment at MCMC] puts you in a different and much better mindset right from the start," he said. "That happens to everyone who works here. It carries us through the day and has a tremendously positive effect on our interactions with patients."

If Celilo began as, in Scott's words, the "template for the perfectly pure healthcare experience," and the focal point of all that MCMC had learned about patient-centered care, that didn't mean there wasn't room for growth. In early 2006, Celilo became one of the rare, small rural cancer centers to be accredited by the National Cancer Institute as a host site for clinical research trials, an acknowledgment of the quality of Celilo's professional staff and quality of care.

The center also continues to investigate and, when appropriate, add to its extensive menu of integrative therapies. In addition to acupuncture, massage therapy, yoga, aromatherapy and other techniques that were part of Celilo's initial offerings, patients now can take advantage of disciplines as unique as Reiki therapy and prayer ties, a symbolic ritual adopted at Celilo from the Sioux sweat lodge ceremony.

Though little research has been done to scientifically support the effectiveness of employing integrative therapies in the treatment of cancer patients, Celilo staff remain unfazed and unconcerned. Even a man as steeped in science as Stelzer does not need quantifiable research to convince him of the value of Celilo's whole-person approach.

"The scientific side of me is very rigid, and honestly I can't make a determination one way or the other if cancer patients who perform yoga or walk the labyrinth or meditate have better outcomes," he said. "And I don't know whether we'll ever be able to determine that scientifically. The only way to do that would be to conduct a randomized trial, and I don't think it would be ethical to deprive a control group of the opportunity to take advantage of all that we are offering.

"The nonscientific side of me says I believe people are being helped by this. We've heard scores of stories from patients and their family members who have had powerful experiences at Celilo that they could not have had in any other cancer treatment setting that I know of. A bad experience in cancer treatment can be a devastating, life-changing experience for a person, and we need to do everything in our power to avoid that.

"My background is in science, but science doesn't run my life. And I know in my heart this is the right way to treat people."

Pet Therapy:
When It Comes to MCMC's Pet Therapy Program, Bo Knows

(Published originally in the MCMC community newsletter, Well Aware.*)*

In its continuing efforts to ensure patients have access to the complete spectrum of tools for healing the body, mind and spirit, Mid-Columbia Medical Center recently implemented a pet therapy program. The intent of the program is to allow MCMC patients to benefit from the scientifically proven therapeutic effects that pets have on people.

The director of pet therapy is Bo, a gentle black Labrador. He makes regular rounds through the hospital, making a special attempt to visit all patients who look like they could use some cheering up. Patients have responded enthusiastically to their visits from Bo.

Well Aware writer Dick Baltus (DB) recently interviewed Bo about his new position and the role he plays in the patient care process.

DB: So Mr. Bo...
BO: Please, call me Bo.

DB: Super. So Bo, what exactly is a pet therapist?
BO: Well, a pet therapist is usually an animal, in my case a dog, whose job it is to make hospital patients feel better.

DB: And what exactly is it that you do to make people feel better?
BO: Just between you and me? Not much. This is a pretty

cushy deal. I kind of wander down the hallways of the hospital and poke my head into the patient rooms. If anyone looks like they could use some company, I wander in, flash my doggie-smile, give the old tail a few back-and-forths, and just hang out for a while. You know, stick my head out for a pat, that sort of thing.

DB: What do you say to the patients?
BO: Listen, I don't work for Taco Bell. I'm not going to impress many people with my vocabulary. With me, it's an aura thing.

DB: Aura?
BO: Yeah, I've just got this feel-good thing about me. It's not just me; it's pets in general. Research has shown that pets make people feel better. But don't tell anybody that. I'm no spring chicken, you know. If somebody at MCMC hears all pets make people feel better, the next thing you know, I'll be replaced by, who knows what, a spring chicken or something.

DB: So, you visit the patients and make them smile. What do you wear, a clown outfit or something? Those glasses with the big nose and mustache?
BO: You're looking at my outfit, a one-of-a-kind, full-body, extra-sheen black Lab coat.

DB: I thought lab coats were white.
BO: That's hospital humor, right? Very funny. Anyway, it's not important how I dress. What's important is that I'm a nice guy with a great personality and the power to make people feel better.

DB: So what do they pay a dog with such an impressive set of skills?

BO: Pay?

DB: Yeah, how much do you earn?

BO: Well, uh, nothing besides room and board. But if you think this is about money, you're barking up the wrong tree — no pun intended. You think Hippocrates had his meter running when he sat underneath that planetree teaching medical students? You think the guy who invented the flea collar did it for the money?

DB: I'm pretty sure that guy did.

BO: Never mind. This is about having a job to do and doing it well. I make people happier, and sometimes I make them feel better. And at the very least, I make them take their minds off their medical concerns for a while. And that, my friend, is all the reward I need. That, and a dog biscuit every once in a while.

DB: Guess it beats chasing cars.

BO: You got that right, Mister.

Thoughts *from* Leland Kaiser

BEING OPEN TO
SYNCHRONISTIC OPPORTUNITY

Earlier, I explained that Mark Scott is an edge runner, someone who is comfortable traversing the edge between an old way of thinking and a new way of perceiving our world. An important characteristic of an edge runner like Mark is that he is open to synchronistic opportunity.

He knows that reality is a dance and he is a dancer. He must dance the dance. The universe follows his lead. It responds to his every thought, feeling and action. Everything he sends out returns to him in the form of enabling life circumstances.

Synchronicity (noncausal correlation) is a powerful ally. Triggering the universe's synchronistic responses requires a high degree of intentionality and very powerful visualizations. The universe cannot respond to ambiguity and ambivalence. When the edge runner projects a powerful intention, he knows the universe will react to his intention, constellating the very events needed for its realization.

Running on the edge makes it easy to lose your way or be caught up in indecision. Should you turn this way or that? The safe course is to move straight ahead with confidence that the path is taking you somewhere. You may not be able to see the destination clearly, but you must move toward it with confidence. Keep projecting the vision of a better world, and move forward. Devote yourself to the service of humankind.

At some point while running along the edge, you will sense another surface adjoining your path (the side surface of the table). By taking a side step, you enter a new surface (dimension). It is a different world with new and different possibilities.

Synchronicity permits easier living. What you could not possibly move by your own power moves effortlessly toward you of its own accord. Your intention and its reflecting circumstances are actually a single event in the universe, although your intention seems to precede its fulfillment.

Synchronicity begins to play a dominant role in your life as you become open to it and expect it. The whole universe is relationship. When you view the universe as a partner, you cease to push against it. You learn to flow with it (Tao).

The universe is actually an infinity amplifier. It takes your intention of whatever magnitude and amplifies it to the needed level for manifestation.

The secret of manifestation is to maintain an open and receptive mind, to observe carefully everything happening around you, and to keep your will locked upon a course of goodness. Often in the deep spaces of your meditation, a vision is incubated and rushes toward manifestation. You will begin to perceive the swirl of activity as constellating events appear on your time horizon.

You are experiencing the thrill of co-creation through synchronicity.

Living on the edge is not a secure way of life. There are no safe places or protected circumstances. You are buffeted by both surfaces at once. As security is lost, potentiality is gained. It is a clear tradeoff. Edge runners would rather be conscious than secure. They would rather make choices than be ruled by the choices of others.

For that reason, the edge is not a heavily populated place. However, you will meet the most interesting people there! At many points in his career, Mark had the option of taking the path of least resistance and living an easier life. He declined these temptations.

CHAPTER 13

KEEPING
THE FAITH

Mark Scott's retirement from MCMC was forecast years before it actually occurred in spring 2002. With the widespread acclaim he and the hospital received shortly after the Planetree implementation, many people within and outside the organization assumed it was just a matter of time before Scott left for his next challenge. It was, indeed, a matter of time, but about 10 years after the predictions started.

Scott always knew there would be a time when his work at MCMC was finished, and that moment finally came one year after Celilo Cancer Center opened.

"Celilo was the purest, most perfect thing I'd ever done," Scott says. "After it opened and had such a great first year, with patients coming from all around to receive care there, I felt I had accomplished all I set out to accomplish as a hospital CEO."

But when an organization's culture is rebuilt around a general dissatisfaction (if not disdain) with the status quo, the organization becomes adept at handling change. So, although a few key players have left MCMC for other opportunities, the quest to personalize, humanize and demystify healthcare is fired by the same passion there that sparked the initiative almost two decades ago.

By handing the reins of MCMC to long-time friend and trusted right-hand man Duane Francis, Scott helped ensure that the organization's commitment to innovation in patient-centered care would continue unabated. In the years since Francis assumed the CEO position, he has maintained the course set by Scott and the MCMC team while adding his own stamp of innovation to MCMC's legacy.

The Planetree concept of patient care and programs like the Center for Mind and Body Medicine and Celilo have continued to thrive and evolve under Francis's leadership.

A hallmark of MCMC is that the institution does not rest on its laurels. Besides overseeing the expansion of the offerings at Celilo, Francis has implemented other innovative programs. In January 2006, for example, MCMC opened an ambitious new inpatient rehabilitation program.

Identifying a need locally for a resource to help patients recovering from a range of illnesses and injuries, Francis devoted an entire wing of the hospital to the mPower Center for Acute Rehabilitation Excellence. The eight-bed mPower unit provided, for the first time, a local resource for patients recovering from such conditions as stroke, brain injury, spinal cord injury, amputations, arthritis and burns.

Francis said his motivation for developing the program was similar to what led Mark Scott to create Celilo. MCMC had provided rehabilitation services on a very limited basis, so the hospital had to send people with very serious conditions into Portland for therapy.

"Just like patients with a diagnosis of cancer, these people were facing life-changing conditions. On top of that, they had to travel 80 or 90 miles from home for care," Francis said.

Like all the MCMC programs developed over the last decade and a half, mPower uses a holistic approach to care that gives patients the opportunity to make strides physically, spiritually and emotionally. The unit not only includes therapy rooms, comfortable bedrooms and a gym, but also a dining room, kitchen and laundry facilities, and other amenities to make patients feel at home while receiving physical, occupational and speech therapies and other treatments.

After mPower opened, it took just one patient to convince Francis of the importance of this new resource.

"Our first patient was a 95-year-old man who had suffered a stroke," Francis recalled. "He came into the unit on a stretcher, literally unable to move. His family and physician were hoping we could at least make him comfortable. But only two weeks later, he walked out of the hospital under his own power. It was one of the most incredible things I've seen."

Over the years, some of the key players at MCMC have changed. Jacque Scott, who was so instrumental in shaping and implementing the nursing component of Planetree, left MCMC in 1999 to become a private consultant. (She and Mark Scott later divorced.) Randy Carter, MCMC's original university program director, who grew into an almost evangelical champion of, and articulate spokesman for Planetree at the hospital, accepted an invitation in 2002 to join the national Planetree organization as vice president of organizational development and strategy.

Before each departure, highly qualified and passionate people had been groomed to take their places, and MCMC has carried on its mission uninterrupted.

In fact, there is a timeless quality to MCMC's effort to personalize, humanize and demystify the healthcare experience. How could such a worthy endeavor ever go out of fashion? However, that doesn't imply that the activities that facilitate the mission are not continuously tuned up and adjusted along the way.

In this spirit, Francis took a long, close look at the storied MCMC University training program in 2006 and detected it was getting a little frayed around the edges. The curriculum had remained relatively unchanged for 15 years, while the environment in which MCMC employees worked had maintained an almost constant state of flux.

For an organization so devoted to change and innovation, MCMC had done surprisingly little to ensure that the training program designed to instill that notion in its employees was still meaningful. But a second factor had moved the training program redesign to the top of Francis's priority list. Early in his tenure as CEO, Francis conducted an informal survey of the management team, asking them to rate themselves in three areas: dedication and loyalty to MCMC's mission; ability to effect positive change; and management skills. The results of the introspective exercise shocked the new CEO.

"The average score managers gave themselves was a C-," Francis said. "That was very telling to me. I was worried that people weren't feeling very good about themselves and that we might be experiencing some burnout. That, of course, had serious implications not only for the team but also for our patients."

Francis concluded that MCMC needed to look at reinventing the university training concept. He said he wanted the training approach to be one that would treat employees the same way MCMC had been treating its patients for years.

"What can we do to ensure that we all continue to feel great about coming to work each day so that we, in turn, can continue to set the stage for creating truly meaningful and memorable healthcare experiences for our patients?" Francis asked.

In redesigning MCMC University, Francis didn't have to look far for help. His first call was to his old friend and mentor, Mark Scott, who had become a partner in Starizon, a Colorado company devoted to helping organizations develop and implement strategies for creating groundbreaking customer and employee experiences.

With Starizon's guidance, MCMC developed a new training setting that was introduced to employees in the summer of 2006. Attendance in the program is a requirement of all existing MCMC employees. The intensive program uses theatrical themes to further expand on Planetree's original notion that employees are on stage while at work and they should always remain mindful of their role in creating positive experiences for MCMC visitors.

"One of the things we've learned over the years, though, is that it's naïve to think employees can turn on a switch when they come to work that allows them to forget everything else in their lives," Francis said. "Through this new experiential employee venture, we are helping our employees learn how to merge, in a positive way, the challenges in their lives with the requirements of their jobs. We're trying to create a holistic work environment, just as we have been working over the last several years to create a holistic healing environment."

Through the new university training concept, Francis hopes to help MCMC employees reconnect with their personal and professional goals and dreams to "add density and meaning to their lives."

"We want to help people remember why they went into healthcare in the first place," Francis said. "If they've lost a little bit of their focus or love of their work, we want to help them get back in touch with how they once felt about their profession and give them the opportunity to realize their goals."

It's an exciting new chapter in the story of a hospital that continues to redefine itself and, in doing so, foreshadows even greater things to come.

A New Model for Giving

Near the end of Mark Scott's tenure as CEO of Mid-Columbia Medical Center, he implemented an innovative program to add focus and structure to the hospital's long-time financial support of important community organizations and causes: the Employee Community Tithing Fund.

While tithing policies traditionally are associated with churches, Scott borrowed the idea to provide a better mechanism for responding to community requests for financial support.

"As one of the community's largest employers, MCMC had always received scores of requests for financial aid, and it had always been difficult to determine how much we should give to what causes," Scott said.

Scott said he wanted to implement a program that added meaning to that process and that was tied to the hospital's financial performance. He noted that the hospital's financial success was a result of community support, so a tithing program would help MCMC return that support in both human and financial terms.

The tithing program is funded when MCMC's year-end revenue exceeds budget. Ten percent of the overage is distributed to local organizations, programs and projects whose goal is to help improve community health. Half of those funds are allocated at the discretion of MCMC's community management team. The other half is allocated using a formula that considers the total number of hours MCMC employees or doctors volunteer to a particular cause or organization.

"Our people are our greatest asset, and we want to encourage them to share their time and talents with their communities," Francis said.

"The Employee Community Tithing Fund is a way of tying our support of community causes not only to our financial performance, but also to the level of involvement of our people. It has given much more meaning to our financial contributions."

Thoughts *from* *Leland Kaiser*

How a Powerful Vision Can Empower All Employees to Make a Difference

The visionary believes that organizations should be self-designing. Only a self-designing organization has the speed and flexibility needed to reshape itself in an era of chaos. Every employee should view himself as a potential architect of the organization.

The organization is only a vehicle for the realization of human goals and aspirations. It does not exist independent of the people who occupy it. For that reason, all employees are potential designers. They shape the organization, and they are shaped by it.

In the past, organizations were designed from the top down. In the future, they will be designed from all directions: top-down, bottom-up, inside-out and outside-in.

Virtual organizations are multidirectional and multidimensional. They are plastic forms that can be molded by any external force and can, in turn, mold any external force.

An organization is a composite thoughtform manifesting in the physical dimension. It is the collective radiation of the people who occupy it. If people have high consciousness, the organization manifests high consciousness. If the employees are docile and passive, the organization is lethargic.

Since the organization is a designed vehicle, it should be designed around a collective vision of its people. Each staff person should feel empowered to make a difference. In the last analysis, authority is a measure of the inclusiveness of a person's consciousness. It should matter little what organizational position he happens to hold at the moment. Seldom is the person with the highest consciousness occupying the highest organizational position. This is a major problem in our hospitals today.

People in leadership positions are often not the most inclusive thinkers. They are given an authority not earned by their relative degree of awareness. In a perfect organization, this would not occur. In an Indian medicine wheel, the leader's qualifications to lead are known by all. Because we do not yet perceive that subtle dimension in our modern-day world, we make mistakes. We often promote leaders because of their ability to manipulate the material dimension, with no thought given to their navigational ability in the spiritual dimension. A top leader should always possess a fine balance of the two.

The new-paradigm health manager uses visioning as an energy generation technique. The vision itself structures the shape and activity of the collective thoughtform.

To the degree that organizational members buy into the vision, they empower it and enable it to move from the dimension of mind to the dimension of this world. Future healthcare organizations will employ small circles of people to generate and maintain organizational thoughtforms. These vortex groups will energize the entire organization. Even a stranger entering the organization will feel the atmosphere and be influenced by it.

Healing requires the generation of powerful thoughtforms in the minds of patients. The healer has the ability to generate and transmit these images and then empowers the patient to continue to energize them through faith and belief in their presence.

Visions channel psychic energy from subtle, spiritual realms to our high-density, third-dimensional world. Visions are a bridge between spiritual and material densities. Visions energize us and expand our intellectual frontiers. They stir our emotions and lead us into the future.

A vision consists of multiple images. These images encode and transmit subtle energy. A human being who seeks the images with awareness decodes their energy, and it flows through his or her consciousness. Unless the image is sought, understood and voluntarily taken into a person's consciousness, it will not discharge its energy. A person who is indifferent or ignorant of the meaning of the images will be unaffected by them.

There is tremendous power in traditional images or symbols. They are connected to thoughtforms that have been energized over the ages and, like a battery, hold their energy until it is discharged by appropriate human receivers. A group of people who call upon the symbol are energized by it. As they become mentally and emotionally involved with the symbol, they add their energy to it. The vision thus feeds the people and is fed by them. A two-way energy relationship exists between symbols and people.

Sometimes a visionary can create a new vision. It is without historical precedent and, therefore, not a well-built thoughtform. The visionary builds a skeletal structure or matrix for the new vision and then begins to share it with other people who become excited about the possibilities and begin to add their energy to the developing matrix. They assist in shaping the vision and energizing it.

Once the thoughtform has developed some potency, it is available to anyone in the organization who tunes into it. Suddenly, lots of people are caught up in the vision and become human intermediaries for its implementation.

Sometimes visionaries tap into old thoughtforms to capture their energy. The visionary gives the old thoughtform a new face, so to speak. It becomes an old symbol walking around in new clothes. The new version may eventually become stronger than the parent thoughtform that gave it birth.

Often, powerful speakers and visionaries evoke traditional thoughtforms and give them a new expression for our times. This saves visionaries the trouble of having to build a new vision from nothing.

Visions are not vague mental images. They are powerful doorways to the inner world. They can also build themselves out to completion in the external world. The necessary link in this progression of images to things is the human being who can invoke the images and release their power in third-dimensional reality.

We can accomplish little without our visions. They can accomplish nothing without us.

CHAPTER 14

A NEW CHAPTER: STARIZON

So what does one do for an encore after closing the final act on what he considers his life's work?

That was the question facing Mark Scott after he informed his board of directors in January 2002 of his decision to retire from MCMC. Scott would remain at MCMC until the following May to help with the transition to MCMC's new CEO, Duane Francis.

After that, his only plan was to jump on his Harley-Davidson with his new wife, Patty, and unwind over the course of an extended road trip across the Western United States.

But shortly after Scott announced his retirement from MCMC, he received a call from Gary Adamson, whom he had met earlier at a workshop sponsored by Leland Kaiser, a healthcare visionary and co-author of this book. Kaiser, as it turned out, had served as a sort of a spiritual mentor for both Scott and Adamson. During the phone call, Adamson briefly described an intriguing venture he was starting called Starizon. That, along with the mutual connection to Kaiser, was enough to get Scott to arrange the itinerary of his retirement road trip to include a visit to Starizon's offices in Keystone, Colorado, so he could see and learn more about the new venture.

Adamson had previously owned a successful marketing communications and healthcare business. He had developed the country's first hospital-based wellness program and one of the first marketing communications companies focused exclusively on healthcare. His experiences with his many hospital clients left Adamson underwhelmed with the general quality of the healthcare experience and sparked an idea for a new company that would teach hospitals and other clients how to improve their interactions with customers.

"The idea for Starizon came from two simple observations," Adamson said. "One observation was the fact that the clients in my marketing communications company were always a lot better in their advertising than in reality. If I could have checked into the hospital ads, it would have been great. But I had to check into the hospital itself, and that was far from great. I saw the disconnect of the brand promise from the brand experience not once, but several hundred times. Even in the best healthcare organizations."

Rather than ignore the problem as an operational issue that marketing couldn't solve, Adamson went on a nationwide search in 1997 for people doing the most interesting and creative work in brand experiences. His travels led to Joe Pine, who was involved in work that soon would lead to a best-selling business book called *The Experience Economy*.

The premise of the book, co-authored by James Gilmore, was that American businesses had entered a new economic era in which every business is a stage and, to succeed, companies must learn how to move from simply selling products or providing services toward "designing memorable events for which they charge admission."

In the new experience economy, companies need to learn how to script and stage compelling experiences, turning workers into actors and "intentionally creating specific effects for their customers." Or, as Pine and Gilmore summed it up on the jacket of their book: "Goods and services are no longer enough; experiences are the foundation for future economic growth."

Both before and after their book was published, the co-authors were leading an annual business gathering called "thinkAbout." Adamson had attended one of the programs and observed that, over the course of the first day and a half of discussion, participants were becoming wildly excited about the concepts of the experience economy. But he saw their enthusiasm fade over the last half-day of the program.

"The last part of the program was difficult for participants because they realized they would have to go back and try to explain this great new idea to their colleagues," Adamson said. "What they needed were the tools to actually make the transformation to an experience business."

As Adamson continued to ponder the disconnect between the brand promise, the brand experience and the need for an organized discipline to facilitate such groundbreaking work, his vision for a new business dedicated to the cause was beginning to take shape. At the same time that Adamson was developing a framework for a company based on the principles of *The Experience Economy*, Scott was several years into putting Planetree's similar philosophy into practice at MCMC.

Over the years, Adamson had followed Scott's work at MCMC via the media and his friendship with Kaiser. When he learned of the CEO's pending retirement, Adamson felt it was time they sat down and talked about their common interests.

Scott and Patty's visit with Adamson and his wife, Leigh, which included a tour of the mountain home the Adamsons were building to house not only their family but their new business, was an eye-opener. Later, the Adamsons would travel to The Dalles to see Scott's work.

"It was interesting to look back on the work we had done at MCMC and realize how it fit so perfectly with the work Gary and Leigh were planning to do with Starizon," Scott said.

Scott had been concerned that he might never again be part of something as rewarding as his tenure at MCMC. But in Starizon, he has found the perfect sequel to his first bold experiment. As noted in the previous chapter, Scott's MCMC experience came full circle when Starizon was brought in to oversee the redesign of the fabled MCMC training program that Scott had launched years earlier. Today, Scott divides his time among his and Patty's home in central Oregon, the Keystone headquarters of Starizon and the road, consulting with a diverse range of businesses.

Starizon has grown into a successful consulting business with a long list of national clientele. The goal of Starizon, Adamson said, is at once complicated and remarkably simple.

"We are striving to enable business leaders to transform their companies, their industries and themselves through doing the work of experience design and staging. We might have the best job anywhere because business leaders bring their biggest hopes and dreams to us with the simple request, 'Can you help?' It doesn't get much better than that."

Starizon has built a diverse portfolio of clients, including start-up companies and small rural and large metropolitan hospitals, as well as large technology and manufacturing companies.

"The only thing our clients have in common is the size of their aspirations," Adamson said. "We have helped clients transform patient and family experiences. We have helped clients create new-to-the-world employee experiences, partner experiences, board experiences, even donor experiences. But most of all, we have helped create a way that leaders can change every aspect of their work. Experience design and staging doesn't just become another thing to do; it becomes a new way of doing all things."

Starizon brings a fresh perspective to the consulting industry by applying its founding principles to itself, both in terms of its work and the environment in which it is performed. That was one of the many lessons taken from *The Experience Economy*, Adamson said.

"In the book, Pine and Gilmore speculate about what a consulting company would do if it thought it was in the experience transformation business," Adamson said.

The authors imagined a consulting company dedicated to creating "memorable events that would enable the client first to experience what it would be like to live and work in a world where the strategy has been achieved and then to actually create that future world."

"That concept is at the core of Starizon's approach," Adamson said.

"When people ask us to describe what we are about, we say Starizon is essentially three things," Adamson said. "First, it is an idea based on the premise that experiences are a completely new kind of economic offering, not just an improvement to customer service, and therefore will require organizational transformation, not just an incremental improvement.

"Second, Starizon is based on the radical concept that we, as consultants, should teach our clients everything we know about the work of experience design and staging, instead of holding onto it as an intellectual property secret.

"Finally, Starizon is very much a place, one that clearly exhibits experience principles at work and immerses a client in those principles as they do their own work."

The home that the Adamsons built in the mountain resort community of Keystone doubles as a sanctuary for their family and an almost magical setting for their business. Few, if any, consulting offices make such a profound statement about the work conducted within.

"Most consulting offices are a lot more alike than unique," Adamson said. "That's probably why most clients never think they should travel to their consultants; they always think the consultant should travel to them."

Starizon, however, is a magnificent manifestation of the power of the experience.

"Because we applied our experience principles to our own company, we saw very clearly that Starizon needed to be designed as a stage on which a unique experience could be performed, instead of just an office where workers could be housed," Adamson said.

Every element of Starizon was designed around the company's theme of "Explore. Discover. Transform." Visiting clients are treated to a highly personalized, multi-sensory experience. They stay and do their work in rooms named Aspire, Create, Imagine, Explore and Discover. This is not your father's consulting office.

"When you visit Starizon, it is not difficult to guess what kind of work happens here," Adamson said. "We invite prospective clients to come here for a day, and very few leave without concluding that this is the work they have been looking to do for their whole careers."

Thoughts *from* **Leland Kaiser**

THE IMPORTANCE OF MAINTAINING AN OPEN MIND

We are living on the edge — a time between times and a place between places, where it is no longer the old and is not yet the new. Edge runners — people who are comfortable on the edge — have a special role to play in healthcare as we continue through this century.

A community always has the resources it needs to solve its problems if it can change the way it perceives resources. What does it mean when you run over your budget? Well, what do you want it to mean? It could mean you will have less to spend in the future. It could also mean you will have more. Change your relationship to apparent scarcity, and you tap universal abundance.

Reframing is, therefore, one of the most valuable things you can learn. A prison cell reframed becomes a launch pad to the exploration of infinity. What one person experiences as limitation, another person may live as unlimited freedom. I guess that is why throughout history wizards could never be kept in prison.

What one man calls lead, another reframes to produce gold. So is the metal lead or gold? Of course, it is either, neither and both. It all depends upon whether you are a junk dealer or an alchemist. And by the way, what makes you think it is a metal? Intuition helps you understand the many forms anything can take.

When you are living on the edge of a society or culture, you must maintain an open mind. Chaos destroys old mindsets and creates the possibility of new mindsets. The function of chaos is to unbind and free bound elements. It releases a tremendous amount of energy. It represents destruction in the service of creation.

However, to benefit from chaos, you must not be attached to old ways of thinking and doing. If you have an attachment to the old world view, you will feel a profound sense of loss as the old order passes away.

If, by contrast, you identify with infinite possibility or have a powerful vision of a world that could be, you are thrilled by chaos and feel a sense of elation and challenge.

Maintaining an open mindset is not an easy thing to do. Mindset provides structure and organizes reality. If you have no mindset, by definition, you would have no structure for events and no sense of an enduring reality. You would be lost in the void.

Rather than have no mindset in times of great change, we actually experience a series of transitional mindsets that carry us from the old to the new world order. Since we hold each transitional mindset lightly, we can easily let go and reach out.

Reality for the edge runner is provisional, tentative and transitory. It is not any more real than he or she makes it. Our intuition helps us make sense out of what is happening around us. With our intuition, we can perceive alternative realities. There are an infinite number of these. Each reality will be true in some time, in some place and in some particular set of circumstances.

Since your mindset precipitates your reality, it is difficult to tell the two apart. This is the reason most people don't know they have a mindset. They assume that what is around them constitutes the one and only possible reality. They do not comprehend that by changing their mind, they could change their reality.

What occurs on the edge is a collective change of mind that, in turn, creates a new reality and a new world era. In most cases, the edge is created by societal breakdowns that become breakthroughs. It takes a lot of courage to move through the breakdown. Many people think the world is coming to an end, when in fact, it is simply moving into a new phase of its evolution.

The edge runner trusts the future and his method for getting there. This kind of cosmic confidence permits the formation of new and liberating mindsets, which, in turn, bring forth a new epoch for planet earth.

Mark Scott is an edge runner. Gary Adamson is an edge runner. I am an edge runner. Why don't you join us and become an edge runner, too?

ACKNOWLEDGEMENTS
MARK SCOTT

So many people deserve credit for making Mid-Columbia Medical Center such a special place of healing. No one deserves more credit than Jacque Scott for developing a level of trust and understanding of all the key principles and applying them to make MCMC what it is today. Her dedication, trust and love for patients, their families and our employees will always stand the test of time as examples for others in healthcare to follow.

Before Eric Rigenhagen's tragic death, I expressed to him that his dedication to his work on the interior design of MCMC and Celilo would always set those facilities apart from any other hospital or cancer center in the world. His spirit, talent and love for the work and all of us will be deeply missed. His death came way too early. I hope he will always be remembered for having the courage to push design to enhance healing for all of us. This book is dedicated to his memory and the joy he brought to all our lives.

My deepest appreciation also goes out to Joyce Powell-Morin, Cheryl Gebhart, Catherine Sessions Whalen, Rusty Kimsey and Lauren Artress for all they did to open my eyes to being a spiritual leader in this field and understanding how we heal as humans. Not just biologically, but socially, intellectually, environmentally and spiritually.

The accomplishments throughout this book would not have been possible without the leadership of certain physician heroes like Bob Staver and Bill Hamilton. Bob Staver's understanding of art, beauty and medicine made a lot of the changes possible. His leadership at the board level has been priceless over the years.

Bill Hamilton's devotion to MCMC is a book in-and-of itself. His love for the place and what it means for the greater good has always been his primary focus. His high standards and principles for healing were the guiding light for all of the healers at MCMC. Without his extraordinary commitment to leading the MCMC medical staff, none of this work would have been possible. His friendship will always be cherished.

Finally, a special thank you to the board of directors at MCMC. Again, without the board's support, understanding, courage and trust, the wonderful story of MCMC could never have unfolded as it did. They were always rock solid, totally dedicated to everything that is right about healthcare.

Where do I begin to thank Leland Kaiser? His wisdom, intuition, spiritual guidance and coaching have given me great guidance over the course of my life — not just as a healthcare leader, but as a person trying to do right. So many people have entered my life, guiding me on each step of my journey. Richard Beckstrand, who taught me that spirituality, faith and business can coexist. Gary Rood, whose passion for work, visionary thinking and the virtues of being bold inspired me. Gary Adamson, whose career path has so closely resembled mine for 20-plus years and who, in Leland Kaiser, had the same mentor as me.

I feel I've been directed by all of these people to do the work I'm doing. Someday, maybe I will understand all of the mindful direction Leland has given me. For now, I owe him for giving me the courage to lead a little hospital in a little Oregon town to do the work of a lifetime.

It seems like only yesterday that I first heard Robin Orr share the principles she stood for that would transform healthcare. At the time, I didn't have a clue, standing alone as a CEO, not knowing which way to turn to find meaning in my career. After I heard Robin speak, I finally started to learn what was important in healthcare. Something beyond all the metrics and bottom-line focus.

There was so much I didn't know about health and caring. But I finally had the determination and willingness to grow and expand my vision of what could be, and I began to understand the principles of true healing. Robin gave that to me, as well as the courage to do the good work we got accomplished at MCMC.

It made all the difference in the world to me as a leader and as a human. I hope our story in some way makes a difference to you.

MCMC's
BOARD OF DIRECTORS:
UNSUNG HEROES

No story of Mid-Columbia Medical Center (MCMC) would be complete without acknowledging the invaluable contribution the organization's board of directors has made during nearly two decades of change.

From the day they put their faith in Mark Scott's bold vision of Planetree at MCMC, the hospital's board members have been instrumental in helping to reshape the age-old notion of what a hospital should, and can, be.

Certainly, none of them could have envisioned what they were getting into when they accepted Scott's invitation to join the board. But their loyalty and staying power speak volumes about their belief in the course they helped plot for their community's hospital.

In their tenures with the hospital, MCMC board members have said "Yes" to ideas and expenditures that would have scared-off other hospital board members more faint of heart. The very idea of Planetree's whole-person, family-oriented approach to care likely would have been deemed by many traditional boards to be too ahead of its time and far too risky a financial undertaking.

In most cases, from the retraining of MCMC's entire workforce to the grim pro forma for Celilo Cancer Center, the financial impact usually wasn't as bad as Scott's projections. Scott always wanted his board prepared for the worst-case scenario. But even confronted with several less-than-rosy financial forecasts, they kept throwing their support behind their CEO. That was something Scott would be able to count on through the duration of his tenure, right up to the point of helping him make good on his promise to hand over the reins of MCMC to the man he felt was the "perfect successor," Duane Francis.

"I have had the rare good fortune of working for a small group of people that have always worked hard to educate themselves about whatever the important issue of the day was," Scott said. "They bought into the vision from Day One, and they've made decisions over the years that many hospital boards would not have had the courage to support."

These are the individuals who served as board members during the implementation and development of Planetree, and over the course of MCMC's continued transformation. They helped bring to life a vision of healthcare few others could imagine.

MCMC BOARD OF DIRECTORS

Bob Bailey

Dan Bustos

Pam Clausen, R.N.

Chuck Harding

Terry Cochran

Phil Kaser

Wilbur Kelly

Wally Wolf, D.V.M

Robert Staver, M.D.

Gretchen Kimsey

Bill Winter